*S*ilhouette

The story of the Little X

Sewn and stitched together by Nigel Hinton

Published by Nigel Hinton

First published in 2009

Copyright: Nigel J Hinton

ISBN 978-0-9550343-1-2

Printed and Bound by
Creative Digital Printing Limited, Shrewsbury

Index of photographs and illustrations

Acknowledgements

This book originally started life as a web-based, historical research project, looking into some of the manufacturing enterprises that have operated in Shrewsbury - www.madeinshrewsbury.co.uk .

Many people have played a part in the development of the website and this book; the first of them is my wife Bridget who is a supportive partner of Made in Shrewsbury. The late Ron Gunn, formerly of Hartleys, was one of the many people with a passion for the things they made and the companies they worked for, and he was one of the main influences in my starting the MIS project.

As to Silhouette, my friends Les Brown and David Cookson have had strong connections with the Company and without their enthusiasm and support the writing of this book would not have been attempted.

Mrs Margaret Lobbenberg was my first contact with one of the founding families of Silhouette and she gave me details of her part in the story, with access to her family photographs and details of former employees who still live in and around Shrewsbury.

The late Mr Tom Blumenau OBE gave me access to his family archive and permission to quote from his own history of the Company, originally published in the Silhouette Express. The early history of the Company set out in this book would have been a lot less detailed without the contributions and photographs taken from the Lobbenberg and Blumenau albums started by Otto Lobbenberg.

In a letter to Hans Blumenau dated June 1956 Otto hoped that future generations may like to carry on the work. He quoted Goethe's words:

"Wohl dem, der seiner väter gern gedenkt!"
"Happy is he who thinks of his father with love."

Acknowledgements continued

Mr Peter Lobbenberg gave valuable background information about his family; he supplied the details of his mother Annemarie Lobbenberg and was very helpful in checking the accuracy of the first section of the text.

Former employees of the Company who have contributed to this work include Pam Turner, Iris Mills, Sarah Griffiths, Corrine Rees, Ray Adams and Aras Gasiunas of Silhouette England. Details of music played at concerts and sheet music of the 1950s were provided by Mrs Irene Cooper.

Chris Eldon Lee has been an enthusiastic supporter of the project and has shared with me the research he did for the play he has written about the Company. Maggie Love organised a number of meetings and conducted interviews with former employees, and some of these have been transcribed and incorporated into this work. Thanks also go to the other researchers and recorders who have contributed.

Susanna Hinton's assistance has been invaluable in setting out, typing and helping with the production and the editing of the work. Susan Caroline, Ian Gilmour and Margaret A. Love have assisted with the production of the book. Lisa Morris has played an important part in the research team and has given practical help in the production of the book.

The photographs and the illustrations have been used with permission of the copyright holders who include the Shrewsbury Chronicle; Shropshire Star; Adrian Maiden; John Rea: J.E.J. Whitaker, courtesy of Adrian Maiden; Wellington Journal; Shrewsbury News; The West Midland Photo Services Limited Commercial and Industrial Photographers Shrewsbury; E.J.Holyoake; and the many individuals who have given permission to use their personal photographs.

Cover design: Mike Ashton
Cover photographs: with kind permission of Adrian Maiden and the Shrewsbury Chronicle.
Assistant editor: Catherine Bynon

About the author

Nigel Hinton works as a chartered accountant in practice. He lives in Shrewsbury and is married to Bridget. They have three daughters and two grandchildren.

Nigel and Bridget are qualified town guides for Shrewsbury, showing visitors the delights of our town. Both worked together on a web-based historic research project "Made in Shrewsbury". They also did research together and played a small part in the award-winning "Wroxeter Hinterland Project". They are members of the Shrewsbury Civic Society.

Nigel published a book written with local historian David Trumper in 2005, entitled "Historical Hostelries - a guide to the inns of Shrewsbury in the loop of the River Severn".

On a Girdle

Edmund Waller (1606-1687)

That which her slender waist confined
Shall now my joyful temples bind;
No monarch but would give his crown
His arms might do what this has done.

It was my Heaven's extremist sphere,
The pale which held that lovely deer:
My joy, my grief, my hope, my love,
Did all within this circle move?

A narrow compass! and yet there
Dwelt all that's good, and all that's fair!
Give me but what this riband bound,
Take all the rest the sun goes round!

Foreword

When I started out on this project as a web-based research study, I had no idea that within a few years one of the companies would inspire a play, a book and some new music. All of this is a result of the warmth and affection that the people of Shropshire have for Silhouette.

It is approaching seventy years since the founding partners came to Shrewsbury, to avoid the horrors of the Nazis in Germany and France and then to avoid the Luftwaffe in air raids on London, to start making underwear in a disused waterworks and an old church building. From the outside many of the factory buildings appear to have survived very well, although they have been dramatically remodelled on the inside.

Silhouette operated in Shropshire and other parts of Europe for many years and employed several thousand people over that time. Each person has unique memories of the place they worked in, their managers, supervisors, colleagues and friends, all of whom made a contribution to the success story that was Silhouette.

In the post-war recovery period many companies all over the country were proud to have "Made in England" on their products as it stood for a high standard of quality and reliability.

I was disappointed to discover that the Market Drayton building with the unique hyperbolic paraboloid roof was lost to redevelopment recently, but of course I did not have to pay any of the maintenance or roof repair bills to keep the fabric of the building together.

As former Shrewsbury resident, Charles Darwin, said in his work *On the Origin of Species* (1859) - "survival depends on being able to adapt to change and the sooner a species adapts the sooner its chances of survival increase." The same rules apply in business and, as market demand changes, businesses have to change in order to survive.

Dedicated to our forefathers

Plate 1

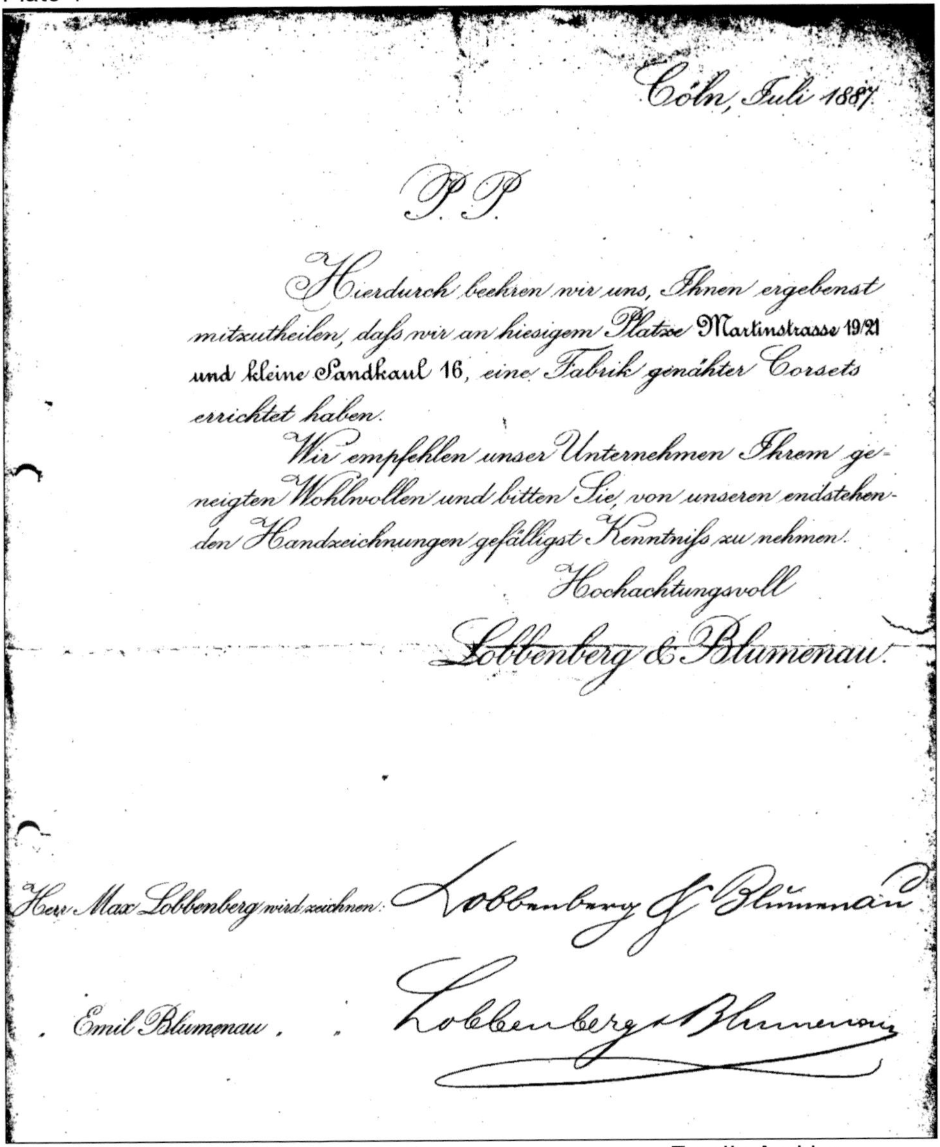

Cöln, Juli 1887.

P. P.

Hierdurch beehren wir uns, Ihnen ergebenst mitzutheilen, daſs wir an hiesigem Platze Martinstrasse 19/21 und kleine Sandkaul 16, eine Fabrik genähter Corsets errichtet haben.

Wir empfehlen unser Unternehmen Ihrem geneigten Wohlwollen und bitten Sie, von unseren endstehenden Handzeichnungen gefälligst Kenntniſs zu nehmen.

Hochachtungsvoll

Lobbenberg & Blumenau.

Herr Max Lobbenberg wird zeichnen: Lobbenberg & Blumenau

" Emil Blumenau " " Lobbenberg & Blumenau

The original partnership agreement 18th April 1887 — Family Archive

Part One - The Foundations in Cologne 1887

The history of the Silhouette Company goes back to the year 1887 when Max Lobbenberg and Emil Blumenau founded the firm Lobbenberg & Blumenau (L&B) in Cologne in Germany.

They had both been salesmen for the Cologne firm of Sebrütes Fried, when they decided to start a business of their own; they drew straws in order to choose whether to start a corset factory or a wholesale business selling laces.

As documented by the original contract in Emil Blumenau's handwriting and then published in the 'Kóluische Leiburg', they founded the firm of Lobbenberg & Blumenau on 18th April 1887.

The partnership was an exceptionally strong one. Their private and business interests were very different but they respected each other and it was said that they always communicated well and never raised their voices to each other.

Emil Blumenau was an outstanding personality in many respects. Outside work, he had a wide range of musical interests: he played classical music on the French horn, and his love of Spanish folksongs. led him to translate some traditional songs, published under the title of 'Cantares'.

Born the son of a teacher in Bielefeld, Emil had an intense interest in Jewish affairs. He was a faithful though liberal Jew and active in the affairs of the Búe Büth Lodge and several times president of the Cologne chapter of the organisation. He was also president of the Jewish community in Cologne. He had a very good sense of humour and loved his game of 'skat' after business hours. (Skat was considered by some as Germany's national card game; there are three or four players.)

Plate 2

Emil Blumenau   Family Archive

In the business, Emil took charge of all legal and financial matters including contracts of all kinds, dealings with the banks and lawyers. He looked after the finances and Max Lobbenberg trusted him completely, never questioning figures produced by Emil.

Max Lobbenberg was born in 1856 in Brakel, a small town in Westphalia. His father died when he was just a year old. Max was brought up in the Jewish orphanage at Paderborn. When he became an apprentice in the banking-firm of L.G. Holm in Frankfurt, he stayed with, and was treated as, a member of the Holm family and always remembered his time there fondly.

Max Lobbenberg's interests were concentrated on his family and business. After business hours he rarely forgot the daily worries of work, although he too liked to relax with a good game of skat.

He took care of the technical questions and dealt with the efficient manufacturing of corsets. His skills and ingenuity were well known and a number of his "inventions" survived him for many years. 'Ski-Federn' and 'Firmi Grips', 'Rapischliesse' and 'Ski-brassiere lacing' were still in use almost 20 years after he left Cologne.

His main interest and hobby was construction. He loved land, property and building; he liked to sit at his desk sketching and planning buildings and furnishings. The Cologne houses of Virchowstrasse 23, Brüsselerstrasse 89/91 and the factory and office of L & B and Ski Mieder at Zeppelinstrasse 9 were the fruits of this labour of love.

Max Lobbenberg had a lot of charm and was also an excellent salesman. He regularly visited the firm's customers in Berlin and the great cities of Rhineland and Westphalia.

Plate 3

Max Lobbenberg   Family Archive

He was a sincere and honest man and the good reputation of the firm – 'der gute Schein', as he said "was paramount". Max Lobbenberg was also a very kind man; he could not bear to hear his children say anything bad about others.

In 1907 Max Lobbenberg took a winter break in St. Moritz, Switzerland. This was quite unusual and pioneering at that time and was to prove significant in the design and development of corsets made by L&B.

It was there that Max Lobbenberg saw, for the first time in his life, people on skis. From the shape of the ski he got the idea and the name for the Ski-Federn or 'stays bent in the shape of skis'. These he incorporated into the back of corsets for stout women. It was then that the name of Ski-Korsett was born, which was the main brand name and trade mark and gives the name to the Ski–Mieder-Fabrik in Cologne. The Company came to adopt the slogan 'Die Marke fur Starke' or 'the brand for hefty ladies'

Plate 4

Skating during the 'Ski' trip   Family Archive

The first business address of L&B was Kleine Sandkaul 16, and after a short while the firm moved to Krebsgasse 1 and from there to the first site that it bought at Brüsselerstrasse 89 (at that time 163). Brüsselerstrasse 89 and 91 were built in 1895/96 in the style of that period. At the front, the houses were private rented apartments. Behind those houses were courtyards, workshops and factory buildings.

Plate 5

89 Brusselerstrasse   Family Archive

Emil Blumenau and his family lived there for many years.

In the basement of the factory there was a steam engine linked to a generator that made electricity for power and light. The engine room and generator were a great attraction for young children.

Zeppelinstrasse 9, the 'Olivandenhof', was occupied by L&B except for the stores and the first floor which were let.

The store at the corner of Zeppelinstrasse and Streitzeugasse was occupied by the M. Lengfeld'sche Buchhandlung, whose owner Felix Ganz was the son-in-law of Max Lobbenberg. The house, built by the architect H Pflaume, was finished in 1914, shortly before the outbreak of the World War I.

The founders were very hard-working men and built up a successful company that commanded respect in their home city. The firm successfully withstood many difficult periods, i.e. the war 1914 – 1918, the inflation after the war and the changing fashions of the 1920s which featured the 'boyish look' when the demand for corsets slumped. Always keen to diversify, they designed and began to manufacture bathrobes.

L & B was always a family-friendly firm and the sons, Otto and Hans Lobbenberg and Hans Blumenau, joined the firm after World War I and became partners in 1923.

Plate 6

Hans Blumenau

Family Archive

Plate 7

Otto Lobbenberg — Family Archive

The next generation brought in some new ideas from the experience they had gained with other companies. Otto Lobbenberg had served his apprenticeship in a corset firm in the United States; Hans Lobbenberg had trained in a straw-hat factory and Hans Blumenau had worked in a department store. With their enthusiasm, the firm grew and eventually employed about 400 people.

Plate 8

Hans Lobbenberg   Family Archive

The Company specialised in corsetry for the larger figure, all bones and busks and rigid cloth, and became the leaders of that field. The firm traded under the name of SKI and was recognised by both the public and the trade as a forward-looking organisation, full of new ideas. They took the lead, for instance, in advertising, which for corsetry was almost unknown. SKI was the first business to use an aeroplane for advertising from the air.

Plate 9

Ski-advertising aeroplane   Family Archive

After this successful period of growth and success, storm clouds appeared on the horizon with the arrival of Adolf Hitler and the Nazi party. Then, in the German elections of September 1929, more than 100 Nazis were elected into the German Reichstag.

Otto Lobbenberg became nervous, as he had foreseen the victory of the Nazis and saw the danger of their carrying out the plans of eliminating the Jews from the German economy. He thought it was time to prepare a refuge outside of Germany, and so he emigrated in 1930 to set up the Paris operation. His foresight had been right: after Hitler's seizure of power in 1933, the situation of German firms under Jewish ownership became increasingly threatened and bleak.

Hans Blumenau followed Otto to Paris in 1936, while Hans Lobbenberg moved from Berlin to Cologne and was prepared to stay there as long as possible.

By 1938 the end was in sight. Jewish firms found it increasingly difficult to buy raw materials; Jewish salesmen were not allowed to travel anywhere and strong pressure was exercised to force Jewish-owned firms into liquidation or sale.

These so-called sales were a farce, because the Jewish owners had to accept whatever money they were offered and, from the little money they received, heavy taxes had to be paid, such as a 'Juden-Sondersteuer' and the 'Reichsfluchtsteuer'. If any balance remained, 90 - 95% was lost in the process of transferring the funds.

Hans Lobbenberg entered into sales negotiations with Mr Karl Werdling of Stuttgart, who was a competitor and president of the German Corset Manufacturers` Association. These negotiations were completed in September 1938.

One of the amazing features of the sales contract was the obligation of L&B to create a "social fund" of 30,000 marks for the non-Jewish employees whom they left behind.

Mr Emil Werdling stated some time later in Paris that he got the best German corset factory for virtually nothing. A short while after the completion of the sale, a political crisis arose following Hitler's march into Czechoslovakia.

Hans Lobbenberg felt the time was right to leave Cologne. He went to Amsterdam under the pretext of taking a business trip to Holland. There he met with his brother Otto, who had returned to Paris from the USA in order to sell the French business as he had expected an imminent French mobilization.

Hans Lobbenberg did not return to Cologne. This was indeed fortunate because a short while after his departure most Jewish men were arrested and sent to concentration camps.

In these difficult times you had to trust someone and one such person was a Dr Spiegel, to whom Hans Lobbenberg left the task of writing up the sales transaction and of attending to the emigration of the aged Max Lobbenberg.

Max could not get over the trauma of the enforced departure and of having to leave his home and his place of work and go to another country. He died, shocked and saddened a few weeks after arriving in London, at the age of 82. It is impossible now to imagine and to express in a few words the anguish and the despair of those hunted people in those terrible times.

Paris
Paris was then the centre of the fashion industry and led the world in style and design, and this was the case with corsetry. Mme Kelly Soiyard, the Silhouette designer, lived there, so Paris had been an obvious choice and at the time the logical place to go.

The new firm, formed on 18th November 1930 with a capital of FF100,000, was called 'Manufacture de Corsets Silhouette', a name that was created by the then junior partners for this small branch factory.

The 'feuille officielle d'annonces légales du 4 décembre 1930' set out the articles and objects of the new Company.

The trade mark was designed by an unknown local artist working in Montmartre who attended tables, earning money by sketching tourists.

Plate 10

| Letterhead with French logo | Family Archive |

When Otto Lobbenberg had emigrated the transfer of capital had still been unrestricted. Later, as Hitler gained more control, it became a major constraint on the new Company. New currency restrictions came into force and the transfer of capital from Germany became impossible.

Fortunately the transfer of equipment, furniture and sewing machines was still possible and the Company started by transferring sewing machines and equipment from Germany.

The new firm was financed with loans from family members and money raised by taking on a new mortgage on the house in Zeppelinstrasse. The parents contributed with loans, even though they did not share Otto's fear that Jews would be persecuted by the Nazis.

The early days of Corsets Silhouette in Paris were difficult because Germans were not liked in France, however the firm made progress over the years acquiring an excellent reputation for quality and delivery.

One of the major contributors to this success was Herman Rosenberg, who had joined L&B in the early 1920s and whose knowledge of ladies fashions and of corsets in particular was of great importance to the development of the Cologne firm. He had been with a leading Paris corset firm until the war in 1914 and his knowledge of conditions in France was of great help in the difficult beginnings of the Paris firm.

Plate 11

Ladies in the cutting room in Paris   Family Archive

Otto and his wife Trudl, who was in charge of book-keeping in the business, enjoyed life in Paris and spent many happy years there. However, the situation for their families and friends who were still in Germany became more and more precarious and the political situation increasingly tense. The danger of war became more threatening as each year went by.

In 1936 Hans Blumenau and later Hans Lobbenberg decided enough was enough and they left France for England with their families.

Plate 12

Shop front in Paris   Family Archive

In 1937, before he left Paris, Otto had obtained the manufacturing rights for a new and revolutionary garment - a radioactive corset. With a stimulating and rejuvenating influence on the cells of the human body, it would reduce fatigue, warm the body and ease rheumatic pain. A patent had been issued in France, including a certificate from the Marie Curie Institute confirming it was radioactive.

However, by 1938 the political situation had deteriorated even further and Otto Lobbenberg felt that war was inevitable. He decided to leave Europe altogether and in March he and his family emigrated to the USA. This was a very difficult decision to make because he considered the

Paris firm was his own. The idea of giving up all the achievements and results of years of hard work and starting again in another country was not something he looked forward to.

Otto returned once more to France to sell the firm and, fortunately, he found a buyer by the name of Marcel Marie, a competitor who had a son who would take over running the business.

London

Hans Blumenau relished the challenge of starting a brand new business in a new location. He needed all his experience and skills in business matters in general, and in corset-making in particular, and he had to acquire new skills and techniques very quickly in order to survive.

He found that British business worked differently from German and French; some practices were not appropriate for the British market. It was a difficult start and for the first few years it did not get any easier.

Corsets Silhouette Ltd was incorporated on 28th May 1936. The subscribers to the Memorandum were Hans Blumenau (£2,250) and Otto Lobbenberg (£750). The factory and offices were located above the ground floor at Angel House, Angel, Pentonville Road, Islington, London, N1.

Plate 13

The Angel Offices   Family Archive

The first employees were Mrs G. Armistead – who later became a director of the firm – and Mr F. Wadsworth who eventually retired at the age of 80, after 34 years of continuous service with the firm.

In the late 1930s there was a craze for health and personal fitness and, as it gained momentum, brands like Slimtex and Vita-flex promoted their rubber, reducing girdles. Being made of lightweight, perforated rubber sheeting, they were guaranteed not to split, peel or crack.

Silhouette became responsible for the world's first (and perhaps only) radioactive corset when, in 1937, Hans was approached by his partner Otto, from the Paris office and offered the manufacturing rights for a 'new and revolutionary' garment - the radioactive corset, 'Radiante'.

This foundation garment was advertised with claims that it was made with fabric "impregnated with radioactive elements – uranium, thorium and radium" - and was said to "give a feeling of energy, fitness and a resistance to chills." Incredibly, it was an immediate success.

In spite of the success of 'Radiante', the first few years of business for the firm were extremely difficult. It took four years of trading for it to reach an annual turnover of £11,000, a figure that it was achieving in less than a day only a few years later. There were no profits during these first years in spite of all the hard work.

When the war broke out everything changed. The Company was unable to produce its normal high quality product range and was ordered by the government to produce 'utility' goods.

Plate 14

Workers in 'The Angel'   Family Archive

Suddenly there was no selling problem – the main task was to source the raw materials to make the clothes and underwear and all other goods that had been in short supply. This was a time when all basic supplies became scarce and food and clothes were rationed.

Silhouette established its reputation as a reliable firm and the Company distributed its finished goods fairly amongst its customers. The

Company's customers remembered this and they remained very loyal when normal business resumed after the war.

Until then all the business had been done without much advertising. This changed following the visit of a stranger who walked into the Angel offices off the street. The gentleman asked for an interview and showed Hans Blumenau an advertisement he had designed for Silhouette corsetry – the Lady and the Gazelle.

Plate 15

The Lady and the Gazelle   Family Archive

He did not leave his name or accept any payment, saying: "If you use the design, it will give me great pleasure". He never appeared again. 'The Lady and the Gazelle' was adopted by the Company and was used on letter headings, in the trade press, on packaging and in window displays.

Corsets Silhouette Ltd was still a small firm and was delighted to be introduced to Flexees through Miss Cawley, the corset buyer at Dickins and Jones. Until the war they had sold their American-produced goods in Great Britain, but they were now cut off from their source of supply and were eager to have their goods 'Made in England'.

After Germany invaded France, the British became very suspicious of all foreigners, especially German-born people. The consequence of this was the wholesale internment of German refugees.

This posed a great threat to the continuation of the business but, as can often be seen in times of crisis, the best comes out in certain people: when Hans Blumenau was threatened with internment, Miss Cawley offered to become the guardian of the children.

Hans Lobbenberg was out on ARP (Air Raid Precautions) blackout duty when the police came for him so they could not take him in. Furthermore, it was fortunately the day the government changed its policy. They recognised that Jewish German refugees should not be considered potential 'Fifth Columnists', so they did not come back for Hans.

Hans Blumenau`s brother Ernest Blumenau was one of the unfortunate people who were taken in before this change and he was interned for many months. Many others were shipped overseas and a great number of those were drowned when their ships were torpedoed by German submarines.

Production of the standard range products carried on at Angel House well into the Blitz but the Company also diversified into other lines, including making gas mask carriers.

Production became increasingly difficult: most of the machinists lived in the east end of London and were unable to come to work when their districts and their houses were bombed. Thankfully none of the Company employees were killed.

Hans Lobbenberg and Hans Blumenau decided to look for a safer place to locate the factory. It was suggested that Coventry in Warwickshire might suit their needs or Shrewsbury in Shropshire; it was thought that the more rural location might not attract the German bombers.

A decision was made and Shrewsbury was chosen.

Within 48 hours they had found a disused pub, which served for offices and a cutting room, a small church hall suitable for manufacturing, three private buildings to house the staff and a large family home. All members of the Lobbenberg and Blumenau families moved into it and stayed there throughout the war.

After Hitler's defeat in 1945 a limited compensation for the material losses suffered by the German Jews was granted. In 1952 an agreement was reached between the families as former owners of the Ski-Mieder-Fabrik and the successors. The firm remained with the successors, who paid an agreed amount of compensation, and the houses at 89 and 91 Brüsselerstrasse and at 9 Zeppelinstrasse were returned to their rightful owners.

Part Two - Shrewsbury: Tankerville Street, Monkmoor Road and Coton Hill

The directors made the decision to move just in time: one week later there were no available buildings left in Shrewsbury because so many other firms were leaving the cities for the rural towns.

Most of the London staff followed the firm to Shrewsbury. They were pleased to live in a less dangerous place and only two staff remained in London, for family reasons. The London staff moved into lodgings in Milk Street where two buildings were converted into boarding houses.

Plate 16

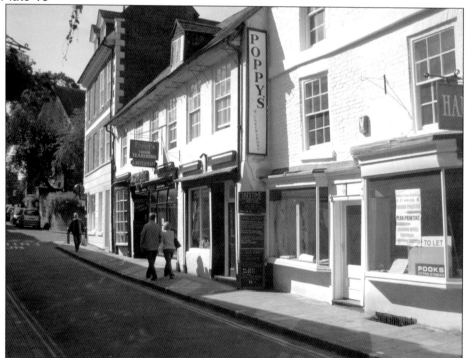

Former boarding houses Milk St in 2009   Nigel Hinton

Plate 17

The church at Monkmoor Road
and Tankerville Street

Family Archive

The factory for the machinists was established on the corner of Monkmoor Road and Tankerville Street.

Plate 18

The Old Castle Vaults   Family Archive

The Company opened a cutting department in an old pub building, the Old Castle Vaults on Beacalls Lane, close to the prison.

Plate19

Castle Walk   Family Archive

Having been cut in the Old Castle Vaults, the pieces were taken to be machined in Tankerville St across the River Severn, over the Castle Walk bridge; for a time an old pram was the preferred mode of transport.

Plate 20

The church opposite the Old Waterworks,   Family Archive

This building was used as the canteen and as a storage area.

After the war was over, it was a few years before the country got back to normal. In 1947 'non-utility' merchandise was again permitted, but there was still a major shortage of suitable quality raw material in the country.

Remembering pre-war connections in France, Hans Blumenau went to Calais and bought the entire output of 'Dentellastix', a high-class fabric, made by Tiburce–Lelas. Calais was still in ruins, but Tiburce-Lelas was partly standing, and, most importantly, still had two working looms.

Through buying the whole production available Silhouette had the monopoly of it in the UK. This enabled Silhouette to be the first company back onto the market with a comprehensive range of high-quality foundation garments after the war.

Plate 21

The exterior of the Old Waterworks in Coton Hill   Family Archive
Today the building houses an environmentally friendly business centre
Little has changed on the outside.

The need for more production capacity came about because of the Silhouette Company's claim that it could fit practically any woman - big, small or indifferent, with big hips or with no hips at all.

This resulted in the Company carrying a wide range of styles and sizes, which created production, material sourcing and stock-holding problems. The London factory at the Angel was re-opened to assist in meeting orders which required all that Shrewsbury and London could produce.

Plate 22

The interior of the Old Waterworks in Coton Hill   J.E.J Whitaker
Courtesy of Adrian Maiden

Plate 23

Christmas in the Old Waterworks

J.E.J Whitaker
Courtesy of Adrian Maiden

Plate 24

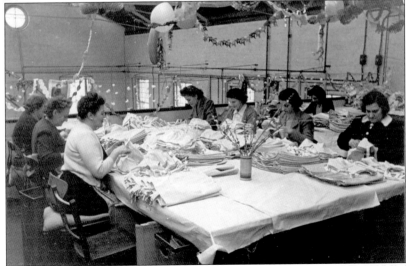

Sewing corsets at Coton Hill

J.E.J Whitaker
Courtesy of Adrian Maiden

Plate 25

Hans Lobbenberg showing a film

J.E.J Whitaker
Courtesy of Adrian Maiden

The family and social side of the Company were important to the founding families and, compared to many other local companies, Silhouette looked after their staff exceptionally well.

The scale of the events grew with the Company and as the numbers increased the venue for social events got bigger.

After the war the third generation of the families joined the Company: Tom Blumenau and George Lobbenberg.

Tom Blumenau was 19 when he joined Silhouette from school in 1946, and after almost four years` training in Shrewsbury he went to America to gain further experience.

Plate 26

Tom Blumenau   Family Archive

At the age of 18, George Lobbenberg had left France to join his mother, Gretal, his father's first wife, in America. After three years he joined the

American army, only to be sent back to France with General Patton, where he landed in Normandy.

Plate 27

George Lobbenberg   Family Archive

Later, George served as a translator in the Nuremburg trials before returning to New York to complete his studies. In 1948 he came to Shrewsbury to live and work.

With this new infusion of energy, the next generation wanted to continue the Company's growth, and make it even more successful. They introduced advertising to Silhouette in 1949 with the slogan "Silhouette Your Figure" devised by the Company's advertising agent Robert S Caplin. Then schemes were thought out to entice retailers to stock more Silhouette merchandise.

Plate 28

Silhouette your figure   Family Archive

The Company's turnover trebled between 1948 and 1949, but remained static for the next 3 years owing to greatly increasing competition. Caplin suggested that the Company needed a place in the West End, as it had a 'West End' reputation.

They relocated the London office to a splendid Regency house at 130 Park Lane, overlooking Hyde Park. The showroom was designed by Architect Mr W Marmorek.

Plate 29

CORSETS SILHOUETTE LTD.

SEND YOU THEIR BEST WISHES

FOR A VERY

Happy Christmas

. . . AND LOOK FORWARD
TO SEEING YOU IN THE

*Spring in
Park Lane*

Until then, the address remains
CORSETS SILHOUETTE LTD.,
ANGEL HOUSE, LONDON, N.1

Card announcing the change of address   Family Archive

Plate 30

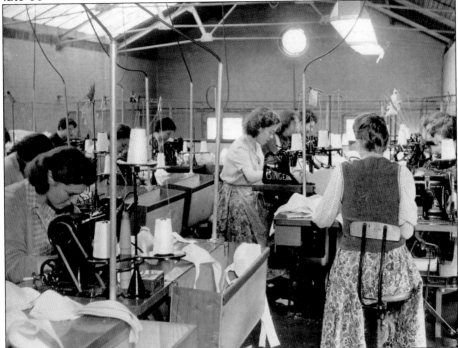

Making bras on the first floor
of the Old Waterworks, Coton Hill

Wellington Journal &
Shrewsbury News

The partnership with Flexees, the Company's American partner, had been established for some time. It had worked well until 1951 when their mutual interests drifted apart. Flexees needed more merchandise than the Company were able to supply, at the time, and they also wanted equity participation or shares in Corsets Silhouette Ltd, which the owners were not willing to agree to. So the business arrangements ceased and they parted amicably.

In 1953 an agreement was made with Peter Pan Inc. of New York, to produce their American brassieres under licence, but under the name Silhouette.

Plate 31

American bras · Family Archive

Further regular advertising helped to increase business, albeit slowly.

The Company placed a whole-page advertisement in the Daily Mirror and a half-page in the Daily Express promoting the "Silhouette Hidden Treasure - improving on nature naturally".

Plate 32

Hidden Treasure   Family Archive

During all this time the Company continued with the small premises in Shrewsbury, consisting of the original church hall in Tankerville Street and the converted waterworks on Coton Hill.

Plate 33

Machinist, Coton Hill   Wellington Journal & Shrewsbury News

In London the Company still had a factory at 'The Angel' where conditions continued to be very congested, primitive and old-fashioned.

In 1954 Hans Lobbenberg suggested that Silhouette could do with, and could afford, a large modern factory and he made himself responsible for planning the last detail of the new facility. This was to be built in Harlescott Lane, next to the railway line on the north side of Shrewsbury.

Hans Lobbenberg was a popular employer and an enthusiastic, intelligent man. His skills with people were matched by a sharp intellect which he used to become Shrewsbury Chess Champion in 1946 and Shropshire Open Chess Champion in 1948. He also had a passion for large American cars, some of which can be seen in photographs parked outside the various Silhouette buildings.

Hans laid the foundation stone for the new factory in Harlescott, Shrewsbury. When the project was close to completion, but before it opened officially for business, Hans went to see it for the first time. He said that to him it looked like the Festival Hall and he felt that it might never be filled to capacity. Sadly, shortly after this he died and never saw his dream fulfilled. The factory was completed in 1956 and it was thanks to his foresight that the Company was prepared for the next and most successful and exciting period in the history of Silhouette.

Plate 34

Drawing of the proposed factory at Harlescott.   Family Archive
Architects Walter Marmorek and Lionel Weaver

Plate 35

Hans Lobbenberg 1896-1955　　　　　　　Family Archive

Part Three - The 'Little X' Story

Annemarie Lobbenberg (nee Rabl) was Hans Lobbenberg's second wife and they had one son, Peter. Annemarie was heavily involved with the design and development of new products and had successfully designed the 'Radiante' before the war. Her total involvement with the business, her knowledge of design and her study of art meant that she was ideally experienced when Silhouette's biggest opportunity presented itself.

Plate 36

Annemarie Lobbenberg, September 1945   Family Archive

During 1955 a material supplier, John Heathcoat Ltd, submitted a sample of a striped lightweight material for evaluation. It was far too light for the sort of corsetry that Silhouette had been making up to that time. Meanwhile, keeping up to date with the American trade press, Hans Blumenau had read about the success another English Company was having with a lighter weight garment.

Hans suggested to Annemarie that Silhouette should have a similar lightweight suspender belt using this new material. She designed a belt with a cross-over front, suitable for the heavier figure.

Plate 37

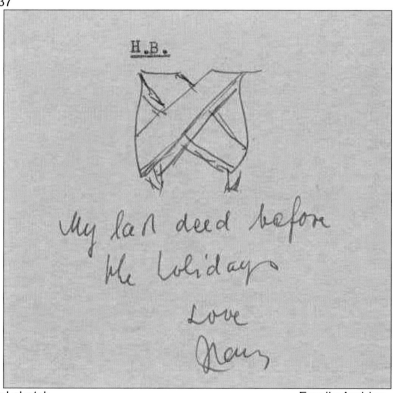

Original sketch   Family Archive
September 1955

Hans went on holiday, and on his return he found that a sample of the girdle had been made, priced up and costed and was almost ready for production.

A plan was conceived that required substantial volumes of sales and production targets of 1000 dozen a month were set. Only a single dozen was the common sales unit quantity then, so these figures were huge by comparison and considered impossible by many people.

It was fortuitous that the new production facility was ready for this great increase in volume and the factory manufacturing management team, led by George Lobbenberg, with production manager Reg Harrison and Bert Spring, procurement manager, were able to fulfil all the orders the sales force could sell.

The Company had a new sales team headed by Mr Gerry Sigler, the sales manager, and they had been inspired by an American firm that had led the way with very high sales and production volumes in the previous year.

They showed the retailer what could be done with American-style selling methods. Buyers were now conditioned to ordering in bulk. Where previously they had bought 2 dozen of a style, they now placed orders for 40, 60 or 100 dozen of the 'Little X'.

The 'Little X' was launched to the public on 3rd September 1956.

The following few weeks were agonising for everyone involved as nothing really happened. The Company had expected immediate repeat orders, but as a result of the excellent sales campaign the retailers had more than ample stocks and so no immediate reorders were received.

Owing to the slow reorder level, the Company considered changing the advertising campaign but then, suddenly, reorders came through at a very high level and the 'Little X' became a huge success.

Plate 38

'Little X' advertising
September 1956

Family Archive

The risk had been enormous. At the beginning of 1956 the Company had £21,000 in the bank; by the end of the year the overdraft had risen to £100,000, and this was secured by a floating change on the assets of the Company.

Great help was given to the Company by John Heathcoat Ltd, the material supplier, who had confidence in the plans shown to them. They gave the Company extended credit without asking for any security.

John Heathcoat later presented Silhouette with a silver statue in commemoration of a "great achievement".

Plate 39

'Little X' award   Family Archive

Had the gamble failed with 'Little X', the consequences for both companies would have been very grave indeed.

However, there was no cause for concern as within a few months every inch of the new factory was used and the Company had to re-open Coton Hill in August 1957.

Plate 40

Packing area, Harlescott   Family Archive

Impact of 'Little X' on the business

In 1955 the turnover of the Company was approximately £400,000. In the second half of 1956, when 'Little X' was launched, the turnover went up to around £700,000 and in 1957 – the first full year of 'Little X' - it went to £1.3 million. In 1958 the turnover grew to £2 million and this meant that in 3 years the Company had increased turnover by a massive 500%.
The offices in Park Lane had got busier as a result of all the new products and it was agreed that a move to larger premises was needed.

So the Company moved to 84/86 Baker Street, London, W1, where they had a total floor area of eleven thousand square feet.

Plate 41

Baker Street, London   Family Archive

The London office was where most of the administration was done, and it was the first place the buyers from the Company's major customers visited. Tom Blumenau was based here and headed the sales and administration operations.

The growth of the Company, the progress made in the years immediately following the launch of 'Little X' and the practical problems this success created are best illustrated in the following extracts from a management report by George Lobbenberg.

Management Report on Progress
1956

The land on which the new factory at Harlescott Lane was to be built was leased from the Harlescott Tanning Company at an annual rent of £200, a low rent for the period, "but", as the owner - Mr. Cock – had said, "there are so many claimants to the money that a relatively small sum coming in regularly is easier (sic) administered than the distribution of a capital sum". The lease ran for 99 years, at the end of which the factory and anything else we might have erected on the property would become the leaser's property – unless, of course, laws have changed by then.

Plate 42

Underfloor heating system being installed at Harlescott	Adrian Maiden West Midland Photo Services

However, none of us worried about these items. The first problem was the move from Coton Hill to Harlescott. Coton Hill was going all out on the production of "Little X" belts, and not one day's production could be lost. Therefore, full plans were made to transfer all machines in one weekend, from Friday night to Monday morning, with the help of a few outside workers, three railway lorries which shuttled between the factories, and with 50 girls pitching in, helping to erect shelves, plug in and test sewing machines (we had left the old line benches behind in Coton Hill). From now on all machines were to be equipped with individual motors.

The impossible became, once again, possible, and one Monday morning – at the end of July 1956 – everyone settled down in this new, shining bright and gleaming factory. One would have expected people to rejoice at the move – special buses provided convenient transport to town; the light was outstandingly good; the machines smooth and fast. All amenities for comfort were vastly superior to the improvised facilities of Coton Hill. And yet - such is the perversity of womankind - the almost unanimous longing was to return to the cosy old dingy quarters at Coton Hill. This was soon to come again, but, to begin with, the floor area was half-empty still at Harlescott Lane, and we smiled at the architect's suggestions of what should be done to facilitate expansion work – for, after all, the floor area of nearly 39,000 sq. ft., was exactly four times the total area of what we had available at Coton Hill, and this was including the rabbit-warren of small offices, workshops etc., which were converted out of the former cottages belonging to the Waterworks Inspector, as well as the Inspector's Offices; not to forget the Sunday School, a former Congregational Church, (complete with organ, duly boarded up, and the inscription "All thy works praise thee, o Lord" emblazoned boldly over the shelves filled with corsetry). Of course, the old church had been occupied by the A.T.S. before we had moved into it, so it was duly deconsecrated beforehand. Across the street, the more mundane waterworks and pumping station, plus a balcony installed by us in 1948, and a pre-fabricated hut to cope with the expanding demands on the Cutting Department, had to cope with production proper.

After the move of the sewing machinists, the cutting department, stores and offices followed in the next few days, and general tidying up began very quickly, at both ends – Harlescott and Coton Hill. We hoped that we could find someone to take over the lease, or sublet the old premises from us. This search, which started weeks before the actual move, continued with advertisements, circulars to real estate agents and a good deal of correspondence until finally – in July 1957 – we were ready to sign a sublease with an organisation badly in need of a premises – and, at that very moment, we had to tell poor Mr. Heller, who had been doing the brunt of this work, that it was a 'no go'. We would need the space ourselves again.

Plate 43

New Harlescott factory

Adrian Maiden
West Midland Photo Services

1957

The amazing fact was that we ran, not only out of production area with the phenomenal success of the 'Little X' belt, but an even acuter problem was that of storage. We had begun to enter the Mail Order business, and this meant that large stocks of articles catalogues had to be kept in constant readiness – for, to disappoint an ordinary customer with deliveries was disagreeable, but could be overcome with a bit of good will, but to let down a Mail Order or Chain Store customer, (and the Chain Stores, where we had had a footing with Dorothy Perkins, soon joined the throng of 'Little X' clients), was an unforgivable sin. The fact that we did give these large clients top priority became of immense value to the growth of the business, and our service-mindedness, of which we had been so proud in our retail trade before, now became a great asset in our relations with Mail and Chain Store buyers.

However, our deliveries to the retailers were periodically poor to terrible, with the exception of those few who "screamed loudest". It was clear that, once again, we had to expand both production and stock facilities, and the obvious thing was to move back into the Coton Hill premises.

The 'Little X' was followed the next year by 'Little Xtra', the same garment with a 2 and a half inch waistband added. This seemingly simple addition created a world of production problems for the factory. The solution was an evening shift of 4 stalwarts, working from 5 to 9.30 p.m.every night, to help to break the bottlenecks in a vital operation, whilst the newly-introduced conveyer bands in Harlescott achieved a smooth flow of merchandise of all types. But the move back to a newly painted Coton Hill, (with new machines, on individual stands) showed us that we had guessed too low – set our targets not high enough – because, even with the new girls who had constantly to be engaged and trained, we were falling behind with deliveries.

Crisis after crisis hit us, and the pressure of work told heavily on the supervisory staff. We engaged additional help, but the training of supervisors became a very serious and important step in the constant battle between the demands of larger production and better quality. For, although our firm was singularly successful during this particular period, the British economy in general was going through a period of recession after the 1955 boom, with the result that buyers and customers became more and more critical of quality and workmanship. We had to battle constantly to make our staff aware of the absolute necessity for quality and neatness, cleanliness and good workmanship – all things which do not necessarily agree with the average teenager's idea of mass production.

Teenagers – our staff had not only grown from some 165 in 1955 to 200 in 1956, to 320 at the beginning of 1957 and to over 700 by the Spring of 1959 – it had also become a much younger crowd: school-leavers now formed the bulk of our trainees. Rock and roll became the favourite music for `Workers' Playtime` on the radio, and the bright blue Pepsi-cola machine in the canteen was more often empty than full. The old guard dwindled rapidly – a number of crises had to happen before they were willing to accept more modern methods of production – swing folders, attachments etc., which were now available to facilitate their work. The youngsters proved not only quickly adaptable, but also enormously willing, and the best of them managed to earn extremely good wages on their fast new machines.

By 1957 the new pattern of production had begun to emerge, and 1958 helped to clarify it. We were no longer a Corset House, but a firm which merchandised promoted articles. This meant that months, and indeed now a full year, before the launching of a new article, plans had to be perfected for the garments to be launched: advertising, merchandising, promotion – but, above all, from Shrewsbury's point of view, materials, design, accessories and, worst of all, the clouded crystal ball had to forecast the quantities required at the launching date. Frequently, owing to Mail Order requirements, new articles had to be delivered well before these official launching dates, sometimes with awkward results. Our retailers had strict instructions not to show promoted garments in their windows before a certain date, and yet the Mail Order catalogues were circulating freely days – and, on one occasion, 6 weeks ahead of that date. Well, we learnt to overcome this problem – the hard way.

Plate 44

Inside Harlescott factory

Adrian Maiden
West Midlands Photo Services

Clearly, more space was needed again – and a decision to proceed with Phase II of the building at Harlescott Lane was made. In the meantime, an opportunity to purchase 2 acres of land, adjoining the leased tract, had been taken (at a cost of £5,850, a high price), and a 5,000 sq.ft. shed which was included in the price was soon cleared out, a concrete floor laid, and filled in no time with boxes, packing material and elastic net from the bulging stores of Mr. Spring. The multitude of styles in our supposedly constantly shrinking range brought with it a multitude of boxes and again storage problems.

The new building extension, which would enlarge the 1956 structure by hooking on to it directly, (a large centre girder had been protruding invitingly for 2 years, in readiness for this move), was to cover 20,000 sq.ft. Of these, some 15,000 sq. ft. were to be used for finished goods storage and despatch, and 5,000 sq. ft. were to be added to the production floor. The temporary wall at the end of the factory would disappear, and an additional monitor would light the production area. The three outside walls of the new structure would again be temporary, just in case. The top of the storage area would be supported by strong concrete columns, so that a further factory of 300 machines could be placed on top of it, should the need arise.

This building rose rapidly, and, by the end of December 1958, we began to move into it. The new factory proper, which had been created by the addition, became a 5,000 sq. ft. area that became a little frightening, even to us, who had seen the rapid growth of the firm. To keep all these hundreds of workers and machines employed seemed a tremendous responsibility. In addition, of course, they had to be fed and the teas administered at regular intervals. This meant that the 'old' canteen had become utterly inadequate. Four sittings for the morning tea, and three for lunch had become necessary, and, therefore, work on a new canteen was started the minute work had finished on the extension. This would accommodate 400 in one sitting, and include not only a very modern kitchen, but also an Executive Dining Room which could be used for the regular medical examinations of young workers; it would have wooden floors and was intended to become a social centre in the evenings.

By now we had five conveyer belts, with a sixth one due for delivery in July 1959. Parties of school-leavers visited us regularly from all surrounding schools, and the firm had become the largest single employer of female labour in Shropshire. Nevertheless, the problem of expansion remained with us as big as ever. In fact, it began to grow in to a perpetual headache – even though an extremely pleasant one. Owing to the changed financial circumstances of our landlord, we had been able to acquire the freehold of the leased Harlescott land at a price of £7,000 in December 1958. **George Lobbenberg**

Part Four - The Factories beyond Shrewsbury

Market Drayton

The sales force was selling the products in ever higher volumes and this increasing demand for its American bras and 'Little X' meant that more production capacity was needed. So the Company set about acquiring land and building new factories around the county of Shropshire and beyond. The first of these was in Market Drayton.

Plate 45

The factory under construction   Family Archive
Market Drayton

This new factory had a 30,000 sq. ft. area, and a 'hyperbolic-paraboloid' roof designed with one pillar in the centre of the building, which gave maximum space and flexibility for the machinery. Production started in December 1960.

When this new facility came on stream the Company closed the Coton Hill factory, but had to re-open it in May 1961, when both Harlescott and

Market Drayton were at full capacity and even more production was needed.

All went well for a while at Market Drayton. Silhouette came up with a new product range and ventured into the world of selling soaps specifically for the washing of foundation garments.

Plate 46

The amazing hyperbolic paraboloid roof   Family Archive
Market Drayton

The stocks of soaps proved to be slow moving, so had to be stored at Market Drayton. After a few months the store keeper, Mr Goetzl asked why increasing stocks of soap were arriving when the soap was not selling.

It was discovered that the roof was moving closer to the stock, and not the stock getting piled up higher. The central pillar supporting the whole of the roof was sinking into the ground!

Plate 47

Hans Blumenau   John Rea
Market Drayton

So in August 1963 the factory had to be evacuated and temporary premises were found in Pelwall House, formerly used as a boys' school, on the outskirts of Market Drayton.

It cost Silhouette more than £100,000 to repair the roof and cost the Company even more in terms of lost production time.

In spite of all the building and extension work going on, the Company still sold more than it could produce, especially the brassiere division and it was decided that more production capacity was needed.

Plate 48

Hans Blumenau   John Rea
Market Drayton

The Company started searching for suitable factory space where there was a supply of labour. While that search continued, the Company went public and was then in a position to buy other companies in exchange for its quoted shares.

Bristol and Cardiff

The acquisition of J.O. Pierson Ltd in Bristol and its subsidiary Frixa Ltd in Cardiff took place in April 1963; the purchase was funded by the issue of new shares in Silhouette. Two million 'A' shares of 4 shillings each were created and a bonus of 1 for 2 was given to existing shareholders. The 'A' shares had one vote to every five shareholders

Pierson's main customer was Marks and Spencer. It was a good acquisition for Silhouette, as the Company did not have the capacity to fulfil their own orders let alone attempt to get orders from Marks and Spencer. In those days M&S had a strict policy of sourcing UK made products for their stores.

Plate 49

The J.O.Pierson Ltd factory   Family Archive

Whitchurch

It was agreed by the management that the Harlescott factory had been built and fitted out to a higher standard than was necessary and, following the experience in Market Drayton, they decided a simple structure with limited refinements was the answer. Land was acquired in Whitchurch twenty miles north of Shrewsbury.

Plate 50

Whitchurch factory under construction 1965   Family Archive

The next factory with an area of 30,000 sq ft was built within six months and went into production on 22nd March 1965.

Plate 51

Long service award dinner   Shropshire Star & Journal
29th April 1977
The Whitchurch crowd

Chirk

The next expansion was into Chirk about twenty miles from Shrewsbury and just over the Welsh border.

Plate 52

Chirk Factory   Family Archive

The doors of this new factory opened on 16th November 1970, with plans to accommodate up to forty-two machinists. There were plenty of applicants, including former employees of the Co-op store, that had previously occupied the building.

Plate 53

Machinists in Chirk factory   Family Archives

Telford

When Telford New Town was developed the Company quickly set up a factory in one of the new units on Halesfield.

Plate 54

Telford machinists   Margaret Lobbenberg Archive

Plate 55

Nightwear and children's wear   Margaret Lobbenberg Archive
production line at Telford

The end of an era: the 1970s

The production had expanded in the 1960s and many more people worked for the enlarged group that the Company had become.

The sports and social side of the business continued strongly. As was common then, and still applies in some areas today, many sportsmen and sportswomen were selected for their skill on the football or cricket field and, if they were good workers as well, management considered it a bonus.

The Company continued to prosper and grow throughout the 1960s with the continuing problem of production keeping up with orders.

The enlarged group with several locations around Shropshire, and beyond, was perceived as the market leader and there were plans for further growth.

Volume production and the economies of scale were seen by the senior management as the only way to remain competitive in an increasingly competitive world. A few companies had started importing similar products to Silhouette, but at this time the Company was exporting to 61 countries.

New factories and acquisitions of companies in the same business were being targeted as the 1960s drew to a close, and the Company was optimistic about the future.

Decimalisation of the currency was planned for 1971 and, although joining the EC was being discussed, there was no thought of VAT.

Silhouette moves back into Europe

In the Silhouette Express in October 1970 it was reported that Silhouette had acquired a majority share holding in Forma. This Company was based just outside Brussels in Belgium at the heart of the

European Community and, although at that time there was uncertainty whether Britain would join or not, eventually we did join in 1973.

Forma employed about 200 people in a modern factory and had been making 'Little X' girdles under licence since 1956. They also made other girdles and bras, many of them designed in Shrewsbury.

This additional business increased the Silhouette group turnover to over £6,000,000 and the number of employees to over two thousand.

Plate 56

Forma work room   Family Archive

Plate 57

A familiar site: a room full of machinists   Family Archive
Note the trolleys for moving product about.

Silhouette in Yorkshire

In the Silhouette Express in December 1970 a further acquisition was reported - G.O. Griffiths & Sons, a lingerie company with premises in Thurnscoe, near Doncaster and in Leicester. Its name was changed to Silhouette (Thurnscoe) Ltd.

Griffiths had been in existence for 14 years and employed about 100 people. They had been one of the Company's sub-contractors for some time and the Managing Director J. W. Swain and the Works Director W. Arnold stayed with the new group.

It was planned that Thurnscoe would produce Silhouette lingerie for which, at the time, the Company had great hopes. This would have left the Shropshire and Cardiff factories to produce even more foundation garments and swimsuits.

Thurnscoe was a mining village midway between Doncaster and Barnsley, and in the area there were numerous villages, with very little industry for women until the sewing trade arrived there.

Plate 58

Yorkshire factory   Silhouette Express 1970

The Griffiths factory was about 8,000 sq ft and had opened in October 1967. Mrs Humphries was the senior supervisor, and one of the employees at the time was Valerie Peat, the British champion sprinter who represented Great Britain in the Mexico Olympics in 1968.

In the same edition of Silhouette Express, Tom Blumenau refers to the main constraint on the Company still being the lack of production capacity, and he explains to the employees that the main reason for using so many subcontractors was to the meet the customers' orders.

Part Five - All Work and No Play

During the research for this book and the Made in Shrewsbury website many people have commented on the very enjoyable social aspects of working for Silhouette in Shrewsbury in the 1950s, 1960s and 1970s.

The Company supported after-work and social activities, with a cricket team for the men and soccer for the ladies. Alongside netball, gardening and golf there was plenty to do if you chose to participate.

Plate 59

Sylvia Brown's keep fit group   Family Archive

In addition to the team sports and fitness, there was a very active social programme of balls and dances and, of course, the Long Service Awards celebrations.

Plate 60

Music Hall   Adrian Maiden

The Company organised many socials; music and dance featured in many of these events.

Plate 61

Awards event   Family Archive

Plate 62

Social event   Shrewsbury Advertizer

Plate 63

Musical scores   Nigel Hinton

The musical scores, as pictured above were received from Mrs Irene Copper who played for the old time dances organised in the canteen at Harlescott. Her husband, Mr George Cooper, sang and frequently took the lead in the Shrewsbury Operatic Society performances.

Until 1952, sales of sheet music determined the UK Top 10 Chart hits, and music was played in the factories from the radio over loudspeakers. I was told that the girls had their favourites and they would get up out of their seats when their idols` music was played, to show approval.

Later the Company brought in disc jockeys to play music in the afternoons.

Plate 64

Silhouette at Morris Cafe   West Midland Photo Services
                                             Courtesy of Adrian Maiden

Plate 65

On the right is Dorothy Edwards who kindly provided this photograph.

Plate 66

Group of friends and work colleagues   Dorothy Edwards Archive

Plate 67

Silhouette sign and friends

Dorothy Edwards archive

Plate 68

A conga line   Brenda Hobson Archive

Plate 69

Ladies` football team, 1968   Shropshire Star & Journal

Plate 70

Social event later in the 1970s   Family Archive

Part Six - Selected Extracts from the Silhouette Express, 1970s

House magazines were seen as an important communications conduit for larger companies. The Silhouette Express had been published for a few years and the following extracts are taken from the 1970s, when the Company underwent some dramatic changes.

Employees were encouraged to submit news items and the usual content included management statements and then some details of social activities, awards and births, deaths and marriages.

In the January issue the Chairman made a comment on the first page about the impact of tights on the girdle market.

Silhouette Express No. 1 January 1970
Extracts from Company News - Tom Blumenau

1969 was not an easy year for the foundation garment industry in general, because stocking tights affected the sale of girdles. In spite of this the Company managed to increase our sales to our customers by just 10%, which is not bad going, under the circumstances! This was mainly due to the fact that our designers gave us some lovely new merchandise for the slim – medium – and fat. 1969 was also the year of the hot summer, and this helped our swimwear business along very nicely.

What about the outlook for 1970? All the garments are selling very well indeed, and our biggest problem for this year seems as though it is going to be getting enough production.

One of the greatest worries is getting enough sewing machinists. We are always getting new girls, but then the girls are always leaving to get married, and then leaving to have babies, so it is a constant struggle to keep our production growing. We are, at the moment, using a considerable number of factories outside the Silhouette organisation, but we would much rather be making the merchandise in our own factories.   So, whatever you can do to help us get more machinists will be very welcome indeed!

This is the whole secret of the successful growth of the Company. Our company <u>must</u> grow, because only by growing can we remain competitive with other big companies. We have to be efficient, quality-minded and at all times be considering new ideas. It may well be that you have an idea which our company could well use. Look around you. Could this or that job be done more efficiently? Is there any way that you can see that the factory or the office could be happier, a more pleasant place to work in? How can the people all around you work better as a team? <u>We are a team</u> and our aim in the years to come must be to work together more and more, with the common end of making our company the biggest and best company in our industry.

Plate 71

Swimwear, new range   Family archive

Silhouette Express No. 2 June 1970
Tom Blumenau

The 1971 swimwear range is now completely designed. It is the most exciting range we have ever had; included in it are catsuits, trouser suits and other glamorous beachwear items as well as swimsuits, two-pieces and bikinis in intriguing new fabrics. We will be showing you some pictures of the range in a future issue. Special customers, both at home and overseas, have already seen the collection, and their reaction to it is excellent.

Isn't it incredible that customers are already choosing their 1971 merchandise, when most of us have not had an opportunity to wear our 1970 garments?

Plate 72

Pamela Turner shows
Mrs Dyas the Mayor the latest styles

Shrewsbury Chronicle

Silhouette Express No. 3 October 1970
Gerry H. Sigler - Director

Most of you will know that we have a London office in which about thirty-five people work. This deals mainly with the selling activities of the Company, including such tasks as advertising, press relations, and the shipping and documentation of export orders.

We have our showrooms which, especially during the swimwear selling season, now nearly upon us, are a hive of activity, when many retail stores, both British and foreign, look at our range.

When, a few years after the war, things returned to normal, and one could freely supply merchandise again, Silhouette was a very small company which had a hundred or so customers in Britain and even fewer abroad. At that time we sold exclusively to retail stores and shops, including corsetry specialists, of which there were quite a few in those days.

By and by, we started to engage representatives who opened more and more new accounts and today we have a sales force of twenty-three men and women who represent us to stores and shops throughout the British Isles. Many of these have been with us for a long time and some of you see them about the factory when we have our sales conferences in Shrewsbury.

These representatives are directed and controlled from our London office through a team of sales managers. They travel to visit our customers and show them new numbers and take repeat orders for existing styles. Behind this team, there is quite a complicated organisation which has been built up over the years, and I am pleased to tell you that today there are very few suitable retail customers who do not buy from Silhouette.

However, as you have no doubt noticed yourselves, in the last fifteen years there have been tremendous changes in the pattern of retail selling in Britain, and it was necessary for us to look in other directions in order to maintain a full order book and sufficient work for our factories.

Plate 73

Island Display   Corrine Rees Archive

About fifteen years ago, therefore, we started to look at mail order, and from small beginnings this has become a considerable part of our business. We deal with all the major houses and you will see Silhouette corsetry and swimwear well represented in the catalogues. Mail order houses are important customers and need a lot of looking after, a task which again is done mainly from London, and where there is a sales manager in charge of the operation.

All of you are probably customers of Marks and Spencer – by far the largest retail organisation in this country dealing with our type of merchandise. It was our feeling that we must have a share of this trade, and it was for this reason that about eight years ago we associated ourselves with J.O. Pierson in Bristol, who are prominent Marks and Spencer suppliers, and today most of their production is made for this customer.

More recently we have started to supply the other large chain store organisations in this country, which are British Home Stores, Littlewoods and Dorothy Perkins, each of which get garments supplied under their own labels, but designed and made by Silhouette. All these accounts are looked after by the London sales team, who closely co-operate with Shrewsbury – where the designers are situated.

Last but not least, there are our export activities which have been going on for a long time, and which are constantly being expanded in many countries of the world. This applies particularly to swimwear, where we are going from country to country, and where, for instance, we are taking part this year in British Trade Missions to California and Denmark, both of which are new ventures for Silhouette swimwear. The field of leisurewear, of which swimwear is a part, is growing fast, and faster than our production has been able to cope with in the past.

We have plans for 1971 which aim to expand our sales and our production of this type of merchandise. It has always been of the greatest concern to us to have available plenty of work for our factories and that is why we try to be a little ahead of time with our selling activities, and not neglect any likely outlet for our products.

This, therefore, is another explanation for the considerable variety of styles which we have to make, because different customers have different requirements. Since we feel that there is safety in numbers, we must follow their wishes.

Recently, the corset industry has been through a very difficult period which is only just becoming easier. Many of our competitors were very short of work, and two or three of them have, in fact, closed down. We were happy indeed, for all our sakes, that during all this period this did not apply to Silhouette.

Silhouette Express No. 4 December 1970
Company News

Obituary

Mr. George Lobbenberg, whom most of you have known, died on October 22nd of this year, still very young. He was only 47 years old.

He had not been well for a long time, but was very ill for over a year. He bore his illness with great courage and hope of recovery.

It was his illness which brought about his retirement from the Joint Managing Directorship in August 1969.

Mr. George was the son of Hans Lobbenberg who, with his great vigour and intelligence, helped to lay the foundation stone to our later growth.

After the untimely death of Mr. Hans Lobbenberg in 1955 Mr. George took over the reins in Shrewsbury and devoted all his skill and enthusiasm to the building in Harlescott, and to increasing our production to cope with the extraordinary expansion, which only came after Hans Lobbenberg died.

George Lobbenberg, therefore, played a vital role in the progress of the organisation, and we will have reason to be grateful to him.

He served the firm for 22 years. All our sympathy is with his widow and his four children.

Any Questions, Tom Blumenau

On Friday 4th December `Any Questions`, BBC radio's popular weekly series made its first ever live appearance in Shrewsbury from the Harlescott factory – staff restaurant.

We were fortunate enough to have on the panel David Frost, Bamber Gascoigne, of University Challenge fame; the Rt. Hon. Richard Marsh, Shadow Housing Minister and former Minister of Transport, and the Rt. Hon. Geoffrey Johnson-Smith, Deputy Chairman of the Conservative Party. The Chairman was Mr. David Jacobs. We had a full house for the occasion with an audience of 600 people and to quote David Jacobs, they were the "happiest and most jovial" audience the programme had ever had.

Plate 74

David Frost, Bamber Gascoigne and Frank Belok   Family archive

The team was asked questions dealing with a variety of subjects, asking for opinions on anything from the question of sex in advertising to the Archbishop of Canterbury's visit to South Africa. Those who asked questions of the panel included Mrs. Judy Roberts, Mr. Robin Allen and several visitors, including Alderman Morland and Kathleen Hughes, Head Girl at Monkmoor Secondary Modern School.

Among the guests in the audience were the mayor, Councillor Vic Pearce and Mrs. Pearce accompanied by their daughter Jenny whom we all know, and the deputy mayor, Alderman Gwen Dyas.

It is with deep regret that we report the death of Mrs. Annemarie Lobbenberg.

Mrs. Lobbenberg started designing for the Company in 1938 when our staff consisted of about ten people. During the war when Silhouette moved to Shrewsbury, Mrs. Lobbenberg and her husband made their permanent residence here and she has been here ever since.

Mrs. Lobbenberg's creativity throughout the years is of course well known, but the transformation of the Company from a small one into a big one based on her creation of 'Little X' was one of her greatest achievements, without which we would not be where we are today and we have cause to be grateful to her. She was widowed at a tragically early age after a marriage where both privately and professionally she got tremendous stimulus from Hans Lobbenberg.

The mixture of an artistic temperament with a genuine kindness towards people made Mrs. Lobbenberg a most interesting person and everyone who knew her well will miss her.

Author's note
[The next article would not have been written this way in 2009, but it's interesting to see how cocktails have made a comeback. I don't think the cocktails came by the jug in 1971 as they do in the bars of Shrewsbury today.]

The Bringers of Hope - M.C. Donovan, Director of Sales

Some years ago, while at a cocktail party, the President of Revlon Cosmetics was asked what his company made. He answered: "My factories make cosmetics – but my company sells HOPE".

The Revlon President was not being cynical – he is too much of a realist for that. He knows that you don't buy a lipstick because your lips are not quite red enough and pancake make-up to hide your wrinkles (if you have wrinkles!): he knows that what you are really buying is the hope that your lips will be more kissable and your skin softer and smooth looking. He knows you are buying "Hope" – the hope that you will look even prettier and more lovely than usual.

Have you ever read an advertisement for lipstick which said: - "Our lipstick lasts a long time"? I doubt if you have. But we have all read advertisements which said something like – "Our kiss-proof lipsticks make a pet of the savage brute!" The advertiser of the lipstick is promising first of all (and most importantly!) that the wearer will be kissed and, secondly, that the lipstick will last longer than usual. But he is also promising that the wearer will become more beautiful wearing his lipstick because it is a well-known biological fact that only pretty girls get kissed!

It is not just true of cosmetics either – it is equally true of clothes. If we wore clothes just to cover ourselves and to keep warm we would all walk around in long woollen sacks – it would be cheaper too! But fortunately for manufacturers of clothes, we all want to look more beautiful and more handsome.

Did you think of yourself before today as a "Bringer of Hope"? Well you should – because every girdle that is designed, manufactured, inspected, packaged and despatched is not just to hold in the wearer's tubby tummy and protruding bottom, but to make the wearer slimmer and more confident of her looks – and therefore more beautiful.

We at Silhouette are not just "Bringers of Hope" because we know our products work. Our girdles, corsets, bras, swimsuits and leisure gowns do make the wearers more beautiful.

My dictionary defines "beautician" as a person who helps another to be beautiful. So that's what we are, all we Silhouette people; we're beauticians. We're all part of a long chain from designers to buyers, to cutters, to machinists, to overlockers, to packers, to dispatchers and drivers in making the women of this country, and of many other countries, even more beautiful.

A word of warning, however: if anyone is going to call Harry Hall, Britt, Reece and our other drivers "beauticians" they should either take out extra insurance or do it from behind the safety of a barbed-wire fence!

Plate 75 (not from the Silhouette express)

Mr Harry Hall standing beside an   E.J.Holyoake Archive
Austin chassis with a body made by
E.J.Holyoake Heath Gate Works in the early 1960s

Plate 76

A Silhouette personality

- Guess Who?

Suitable replies to

the editor please.

"If you know him there are no prizes for guessing Dave Cookson who worked in
the purchasing department with Bert Spring."

Silhouette Express 1973

Silhouette Express Issue No.11 January 1973
Frank Belok MD

Our travelling fashion show teams - like a circus - returned to Harlescott to give its last performance of the year in front of the home audience. Some 700 enthusiastic people turned up and everybody enjoyed the show. That included Mr. Searles and the models.

Our salesmen have also achieved a satisfying performance. They broke the record for spring pre-sales and the 'Performing Miracles' set the pace. The stage is set for a grand spring. Now all we have to do is to deliver the merchandise and help our customers, by advertising, to move the goods off the shelves.

However, not everything is moving like clockwork. In spite of the outstanding support from our staff in all our factories, it does not look as though we shall be able to produce all the merchandise that is required to be sent to retailers and Mail Order Houses before the television campaign breaks. One or two styles are "thin", and the supporting stock probably not quite adequate. You know how frustrating it is for a customer to go to a shop for an advertised article and find that it is not in stock. Rather than waste some television spots, we have now decided to postpone the commencement of the series by a fortnight, to Monday 19th February.

Silhouette Express Issue No. 12 December 1973
F.C.Belok MD

Like most of you, I expect bad news when I open the paper nowadays, so I will write only about the more pleasant aspects of the year 1973.

I will, therefore, not dwell on the fact we have lost ground with one or two of the Mail Order customers and that it is the only reason why we shall not meet our budget – but I take some delight in telling you that we have increased our sales of our bras by over one third. Both the swimwear and leisurewear divisions have made more than healthy progress. Our retail representatives, supported by merchandise acceptable in terms of styling and quality and by reasonable deliveries, have had an excellent year.

Of course, we have had delivery problems. In a year when the school leaving age was raised – thus cutting off 50% of our traditional labour supply – these were to be expected. The labour turnover has also increased in an overheated inflationary economy. By vigorous campaigning, however, and exploring new avenues, we can claim considerable success in manpower management. We pioneered, nationally, the Mums`shift; we introduced twinning and outworkers into production vocabulary, and by these means, have not only held our own but increased production by 10% over the volume of 1972.

Quite a number of us will be able to look at our achievements in 1973 with pride but few will be sorry to see it pass in to history.

What about next year? It will take a braver man than I to make predictions.

The business was slowing down and production finally got ahead of orders. The Company continued to welcome many visitors including members of parliament, local mayors and other dignitaries.

As far as the outside world was concerned, it was business as usual, with cartoons and news of births, deaths and marriages in the Silhouette Express and local papers.

Plate 77

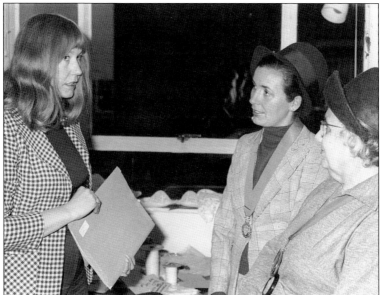

Eileen Greatorex welcomes visitors in 1976   Family Archive

Plate 78

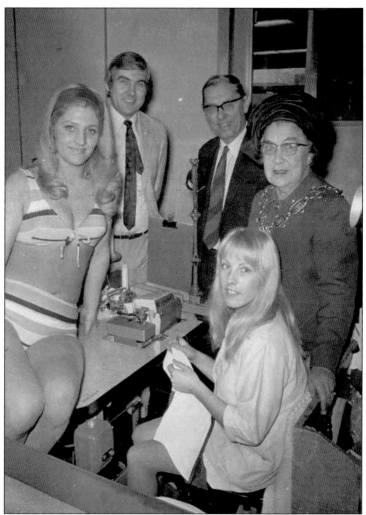

Pauline Wood, Les Brown, Frank Belok,   Shrewsbury Chronicle
Mayor Edith Parsonage & Nettie Roberts

The later years of the 1970s saw a complete change in the fortunes of the Company.

Authors note: This is not taken from Silhouette Express

Hans Blumenau the founder of the UK Company passed away on 24th February 1976. His son Tom had been Chairman of the Silhouette Group of Companies for some time and was the last remaining link with founding partners.

The business continued to fall as the demand for the Company's traditional products evaporated and the new lines that were introduced did not sell in the volumes needed to cover the costs.

Production lines were stopped and instead of a shortage of workers there were too many people, and so short-time working and redundancies were implemented.

Plate 79

Silhouette Sports – 'for that winning look'   Family Archive
Paul Heron, Frank Belok, A Jupp, Clive Wells

The Company continued the search for new products and on 5th October 1978 Silhouette launched a range of sportswear as Silhouette Sports - `for that winning look'.

Part Seven - The Recollections

These are the transcribed stories of some of the people associated with, and who worked at, Silhouette from the early days until it closed.

Tom Blumenau OBE
1927 - 2009

We left Germany in 1936 as one of the last families to get out with our business machinery. Annemarie Lobbenberg escaped from Cologne around the same time.

In England, when war broke out they interned many German refugees in the Isle of Man. My family got as far as the police station but the police realised the loss of employment if the factory bosses were sent away.

Otto Lobbenberg was a professional pessimist and went to the USA.

In my time in the UK I have never come across anti-Jew or German feelings.

Hans Blumenau was a very nice man, straightforward, honest and well-respected. A quiet and very private man who was very fond of classical music, I can see him now continually playing and listening to classical records.

Ski corsets had whalebones – very uncomfortable. Father went to France to buy heavy elastic lace, which did away with bones. But it was very warm. So 'Radiante' was developed to help cure rheumatism. We developed an elastic range which did away with bones.

When the bombing started I recall a bus full of ladies and their budgies evacuated to Shrewsbury where we went to live. I went to school and I received Montgomery at my School Speech Day - a humorous moment in a serious time.

Later I joined the Company and went to train in USA for 9 months to study the American way of doing things. The American company Playtex sold rubber girdles in dispensers. We copied their strategy.

'Little X' was the firm's salvation and all our futures depended on it. We put so much money into advertising; we would have gone bust if it hadn't worked. A Saturday morning workforce was assembled to deal with reorders that never came because they'd been persuaded to take so many items in the first place.

The Harlescott factory was built before the success of 'Little X'; the factory was funded by the flotation of the Company. 'Little X' paid for the Market Drayton factory. One pillar was a great advantage for more floor space and ideal for conveyor belts. It was something completely new and great PR for the Company - until it sank.

Following a TV broadcast by Peter Benenson the founder of Amnesty International, I had a conversation with George Lobbenberg and we both agreed to get involved with Amnesty International locally. So I started a branch in St John's Wood, London and George started the branch in Shrewsbury.

Father (Hans) hated the stock exchange and borrowing money.

'One big family' was our philanthropic philosophy for the workforce. This was not due to the escape from Germany; we had a major horror of unemployment and so we felt a great benevolence towards our workforce.

We diversified and got new customers like Pippa Dee who grew into a most important customer selling via house parties, with distribution by post. But when there was a national postal strike it finished them off. I recall they did pay for their products but we lost the business. We had geared up and employed a lot of people on their lines, so the loss of the customer was serious. We had stopped being a clothing firm and had become an industry.

I recall that Christine Keeler, who was involved with the John Profumo affair, was a Silhouette model.

Hans Blumenau was a morning suit man. He usually wore pinstripe trousers and black coat. He had tiny handwriting for accounts and was a man devoid of a sense of humour.

Hans Lobbenberg, an extrovert, was an excellent chess player, a teddy bear of a man 5'9" tall, overweight, tubby, with shoulders back. Both men had heavy German accents. (Annemarie Lobbenberg over anglicised her vowels).

As outsiders we felt there was a more tolerant community in Shrewsbury than in a big city.

Plate 80

Tom Blumenau, London 2009   Nigel Hinton

Author's note
Sadly Tom Blumenau died on 5th September 2009. His work with Amnesty had continued until his death. He had also been a trustee of Prisoners of Conscience. He was rewarded for his work with an OBE in the New Year's Honours of 2002.

Peter Lobbenberg

Hans Blumenau sponsored us out of Germany; the Lobbenberg family came in December 1938, and we owe our lives to Hans Blumenau who got us out just in time.

I can see machinists in the middle of London and I recall watching the trams go up Pentonville Rd. We spoke German at home and English in the factory. What language should we speak in the garden?

We moved to Shrewsbury and the two families lived in a large house, on Berwick Road.

Silhouette became a magnet for Jewish refugees. My father Hans rode to Tankerville Street on his bike. I recall Leo Borger used to sit me on the cutting table and cut my hair.

Hans Lobbenberg got called up to go to the Isle of Man, as many German men were interned there during the war, but as he was a fire warden at the time and an employer he was excused.

Annemarie Lobbenberg was born Austro-Hungarian (now Czech) and was the daughter of a doctor. She was an art student in Vienna and may have learned anatomy of the abdomen from human life classes.

She and Hans came to England in 1938 but her mother was unable to leave Holland, where she was living by then, and she chose to stay. She died in Auschwitz in 1944.

Annemarie could look like, and play the part of, a real Grande Dame but she was soft and vulnerable inside. She had a distinctive stance and posture. Her head and neck were very posed and she looked wonderful in hats. "Silhouette is my life" she often said.

Katherine Whitehorn interviewed Annemarie in Shrewsbury for the Observer; it was a celebration of female power and design. Annemarie knew Percy Thrower and was a big gardener; she also knew Hilda

Murrell, a rose nursery owner in Shrewsbury, and bought her roses from her.

Plate 81

Annemarie with Otto Lobbenberg   Family Archive

Annemarie laid out the design of the flower beds in front of the Silhouette factory. She was a member of the Horticultural Society and also played bridge at Shropshire County level.

Annemarie Lobbenberg was the designer and worked with manufacturers on new materials; this led directly to the design of 'Little X' and the move away from corset to girdle. The material itself was designed in collaboration with a Belgian company called Rouquinet. At the exhibition "Exposition Internationale" in Brussels in 1956, Madame Rouquinet, a very grand lady, invited Annemarie and me to the show. Rouquinet material was designed and developed in collaboration between two companies and incorporated in 'Little X'. Heathcoat's factory in Coalville, Leicestershire made it in the UK under licence.

Silhouette came to be managed from a London perspective as it had grown and had a number of locations. The 1970s postal strike was bad for business, bad for payments and ruined mail order. Pippa Dee was a big customer and the strike caused them to fail and they went down "owing Silhouette a packet". This was not a fatal blow but it was one of the many things that helped the decision to sell.

Margaret Lobbenberg

I had moved away from Shrewsbury on my first marriage and returned as a divorced Mrs. Milne; previously I was Margaret Thomas.

I recall the 'Little X' being introduced when I was working in London. That was in the mid 1950s, and I remember seeing the posters in the London underground during my time commuting. Also, I knew a little about Silhouette from my links with Shrewsbury.

On my return to Shrewsbury I had to go out to make my living and spent time searching for a job similar to my previous role in London. This of course is difficult in a rural town away from the City but a vacancy became available within Silhouette.

I reluctantly went for an interview because I did not expect to enjoy the work. But Silhouette was well known for recognising good workers and enabling progression within the Company for appropriate staff, so I went along without any great expectations.

During my interview, I felt rather upset when, rather rudely, a chap walked into the room whilst I was replying to a question I had been asked and just stared at me without saying anything. I thought to myself there was no way I wanted to work for a Company that allowed this sort of thing to happen.

I really surprised myself by accepting the role and found that I loved the work at Silhouette. I worked on Littlewoods business, processing and expediting their orders; they were big customers. I also did accounts for the mail order section. I liked the people I worked with, and the Company was a good one to work for.

After a happy year and a half I received my notice to stop working for Silhouette, although this wasn't the end of my involvement. The chap who had so rudely interrupted my interview, previously, was soon to be my husband. A relationship had blossomed between George Lobbenberg and me, and it was certainly not considered appropriate for the senior staff to be involved with the workers romantically.

We had a whirlwind romance and then George came home one day and suddenly asked me what I was doing on Saturday? We went to town, gathered our mothers and stepmothers-in-law and went to the registry office to get married quickly and quietly.

When Silhouette expanded to include the factory in Market Drayton I remember being taken to see the new factory with the special roof. It was fantastic. Tom Blumenau was visiting with his son, Anthony; he must have been about ten or eleven at the time. He wanted to have a look at his heritage or what he thought it would be. I can see him now with his hands behind his back, standing in front of the fire. When I asked "how was your day?" he replied "very nice. I was particularly impressed by the hyperbolic paraboloid roof". I remember thinking "you little s***"; I could not get my tongue around the words at all. As a result of him saying it with such ease, I spent the next two days going around the house saying hyperbolic, hyperbolic, until I could say it with the same ease!

When the roof collapsed the Company moved into Pelwall House; it really was a warren with people and machines fitted in wherever possible. I'm not sure how long they were there but I do remember the House having the most beautiful gardens which made up for some of the inconvenience for the staff. George would say "come and have a look at where we have moved the machinists to." I did, when all the rhododendrons and azaleas were in bloom. It was just magnificent.

I filled the back of the car with flowers. I remember wandering around the grounds saying "this will look nice in the sitting room" and "oh what a good colour for the hall." George came out from his meeting perplexed at his wife's behaviour, seeing the car filled with flowers.

Plate 82

George and Margaret Lobbenberg   Margaret Lobbenberg Archive

I still see some good friends I made at Silhouette. I think something was lost when the small family business became an international success.

I now run a bed and breakfast business in Shrewsbury, and whenever I have German visitors they see my marital name and assume I am a German. Then I tell them of my happy connections with Silhouette and my wonderful time with George.

PAMELA TURNER
Designer and Swimwear Specialist

I started work at Silhouette in 1946 at the factory on the corner of Tankerville St and Monkmoor Road. Silhouette was already established here, of course, because they came up from the Angel in London. A lot of the people who worked with them in London came up to Shropshire too. A couple of houses in town were bought to house these workers initially, all living together.

The cutting room was in Severn Street, Castlefields; I remember we had an odd job man who used to wheel the cut work to the factory over the Castle Walk and over the River Severn to Tankerville St. At one stage he had to use a pram because of the shortages after the war.

Plate 83

Machinists at Coton Hill   J.E.J Whitaker courtesy Adrian Maiden

The original machines we had were made by Singer - they were large industrial machines, black with gold writing on them. When I first came, we worked on long benches with sewing machines on them. A belt would drive all the machines on the bench and I learned how to replace these belts when they broke, as part of my role with the Company.

I remember Hans Blumenau being the sales director; he was based in London. Hans Lobbenberg, based in Shrewsbury, was a big, warm sort of man; everybody loved him.

I can see Hans Lobbenberg, 'Lobby' as we used to call him, walking across the road with a big cigar in his mouth and corseted suspenders dangling from his arms.

In the early days the corsets used to be sent to us for repair. We had a lady who specialised in repairing them for customers. Some corsets had holes in them, needed patches, or they needed bones replacing. We always ensured the corsets were cleaned before they were sent back to the customer.

After working at Silhouette for a number of years in different departments, I was given the opportunity of training as a designer at Leicester Polytechnic. On my return I joined the design team, which was Annemarie Lobbenberg, and myself: she specialised in corsetry and I specialised in bra design.

The design department grew as the product ranges increased into swimwear, cruise wear and leisure wear. Eventually there were five designers who had their own cutters and machinists.

Plate 84

Swimwear models Pauline, PamTurner
Judy Roberts with Pat

Wellington Journal
Shrewsbury News

Judy Roberts was the first departmental model and was a trained cutter who went on to manage her own pattern-grading department.

Designing a Range

Inspiration came from various sources: a piece of material would lend itself to a particular style, and sometimes other fashion items would inspire a design. Mainly, the work involved sketching out an idea and working and reworking the idea until it resolved into a commercial design.

With swimwear I used to do many sketches, and occasionally I would wake in the middle of night with a good idea and do a sketch there and then.

One of these inspirations resulted in a swimsuit we called 'Millicent'. This was a swimsuit that appeared to be a two-piece costume because the centre piece was a see-through mesh fabric; this was ideal for a person who wanted to wear a bikini but who was not quite confident enough.

Sometimes new designs would start with a trip to Paris where we would buy prints on paper of what was currently fashionable. Back at the factory we would photograph the print and then project the image onto a model wearing a plain white swimsuit. From this we could determine the ideal scale of the print, and then we would make up the print in contrasting colourways to choose the final four or five colour combinations. These would be given to cloth manufacturers such as Courtaulds who would transfer our final design onto a suitable cloth.

We also sourced ready-printed stretch fabric materials from Italy, Germany, Switzerland and Austria. I had to go to Milan in January, which wasn't very nice at that time of year, to choose material and I also went to trade fairs in Frankfurt, Paris and Cologne, mainly to see what other companies were doing and what other people were selling.

Every new material and every new style would be given a wash and wear practical test by the factory girls. They would wear them over several weeks and wash them several times, and then return them to the quality department who would assess the durability of the new design.

The swimwear was given a swim test usually at Market Drayton outdoor pool where the girls were given a number of costumes to try out for suitability of material and practicality of the design.

We made Peter Pan bras under licence from the American company, based in New York. I had the chance to go to New York and spent about 6 to 8 weeks with them. This was my first experience of working outside Silhouette and I took the opportunity to visit several American companies whilst I was there.

Later the companies disagreed and a law suit was brought by Peter Pan against Silhouette. We had to go to the Law Court in London to give evidence there and, although Silhouette lost that case, we were able to continue with the design of new products.

Plate 85

Judy Roberts at Market Drayton Lido   John Rea

Plate 86

Swimwear at Christmas   Shrewsbury Chronicle

As we were one of the biggest suppliers of swimwear in the country and we were familiar with corsetry materials, we were asked by DuPont to test materials under factory conditions and develop the uses of Lycra and other materials for the swimwear market. We put a 'Little X' panel in the front to improve the shape of our customers.

To produce a range for the season we would have the girls make samples and agree amongst ourselves which were best and get together about forty garments. When ready, we would present them to the sales director and his senior sales staff with George Lobbenberg and other people from the manufacturing side.

We would show the new range on a model like Judy and they would make a suggestion, perhaps preferring one material over another, and, if suitable, we would then incorporate their suggestions and end up with an agreed product range. We would sometimes have up to four meetings like that for every range.

Having agreed a range with the management, we put on a fashion show once or twice a year for all the girls to see what they would be working on. They worked on individual components so they did not always see what the finished items were like.

Then we made the samples for the reps to use when selling the new range. Getting it right was important because fashion changes very quickly. Our reps always used to wear smart suits with bowler hats and brollies, as was appropriate to the customers we had. As time went by and fashions changed, the dress code became more relaxed.

A few other things I remember that happened in the factory over the years: George Lobbenberg was a supporter of Amnesty International and once a year Joan Heath organised some of the girls to make things out of redundant lace and waste and scrap material in their own time. We would sell these items in the canteen, with the proceeds going to Amnesty International and Loppington House.

We had a lot of people who had arrived from Jamaica in the 1950s; many of them lived in the Wellington area. Silhouette organised a coach to bring them to work in the morning, and a lady called Margaret looked after them and showed them what to do.

Plate 87

Fashion Show for the staff   Family Archive

The design department used to have themed parties in the canteen at Christmas. At one them with a 'South Sea Island' theme, I remember Tom Parker dressed up as a fisherman in a loin cloth, with his skin covered in gravy browning. Everywhere he sat he left an impression of gravy browning!

There were the Silhouette Follies at Christmas time and these were led by a man called Fred Wadsworth; he was the cutting room manager. He played the piano and had us sing the 'Woody Wood Pecker' song. I recall Beryl Wainwright dressing up as Carmen Miranda and someone else danced the black bottom as part of 'Dancing through the Ages'.

For a few years we used to dress the Music Hall in Shrewsbury for the Press Ball. In our own time we got some camouflage netting from the barracks. The press boys hung it from the ceiling and we did a whole underwater scene with fish and mermaids painted on cardboard and paper arranged around the walls of the Music Hall.

I made a career move too: I went to work for another company called Ladies Pride, I was a designer, with a title of director designate. Shortly afterwards I moved to Courtaulds. I soon returned to Silhouette to take over the nightwear and children's wear division for M&S. This was based in Halesfield in Telford, where once again I had to build up a design department from scratch.

Eventually I got a bit fed up with the travelling because I used to have to go to London at least twice a week to visit customers, including Tesco and M&S. So I decided to leave and started my own fashion business on Wyle Cop, Shrewsbury. Generally, my memories of my time at Silhouette are very happy ones.

Iris Mills formerly Hennessey
Administration

I was at Silhouette from about 1957 until the factory was taken over and sold off in 1982.

I was looking for some work which wasn't particularly engrossing or complicated and they were advertising for students at the Coton Hill factory to pack up the 'Little X' garments they had been making for months and months.

The packaging had arrived suddenly and there were many thousands of these things which needed packing. They had all been made in four dozen lots at Coton Hill and they were shipped up to what was then a building site in Harlescott Lane. A small section of it was roofed over to contain the hundreds and thousands of these garments which were just in piles of four dozen.

When I went to the interview I said to the manager Reg Harrison, that I was not a student and asked if there was any reason why I could not come along. He said anybody could come. The Company just thought August was a particularly good time for students. So, if I wanted to come to start at the factory on Monday morning up at Harlescott Lane I could.

When I arrived I found that there was a team of 18 or 20 girls without a supervisor. "Well I will put the team together ", I said, as I had had some business experience. The work was supposed to last about three months, until the backlog had been cleared.

(That temporary job ended twenty five years later, and I had seen many changes over my time there.)

The first job was to sort out the packing backlog. The box was like a triangle sliced off at the top - the designers had put this package together and the idea was to create some sort of visually interesting and eye-catching point. `Point of sale interest` they would call it now, wouldn't they? It was black and white basically with a black and white photograph on the front and back, and we were to stick little labels on the end with the size and the price: 39s 11d, an old penny short of two pounds.

Plate 88

Packing Department

Shrewsbury News
& Wellington Journal

The Company ran extremely efficiently because of the family involvement and the small number of people who were actually managing the departments.

The managers would meet in the morning with George Lobbenberg; he saw every piece of mail that came into Silhouette. He would have an open meeting between eight and nine o'clock and deal with the main issues of the day.

Then he sent the managers off to their job. Having been entrusted with the work they were given, either in production or design or administration, they were left to get on with it, although Mr George was always available with help and advice if needed.
.

There was a feeling that everyone was caught up in the excitement of this rather splendid Company. Its success was a result of this open management style: we were a small team that communicated well and worked hard.

We had 'old fashioned values' as you would say today. As well as working hard for the Company and looking after customers, we put on a children's Christmas party every year, and the girls would collect small amounts of money for the bosses' children as a sign of their appreciation of the Company.

We also ran a summer fair in the village at Harlescott where everybody took over a stall just to involve the local people. The Company grew and was very successful, so successful we went to the stock market and it became a publicly owned company.

The girls worked extremely cheerfully together, and we also had a social club which was very successful, based in the new canteen.

So if we wanted a social function we had a ready-made place. We employed the catering staff, and the food was really quite splendid. We hosted the BBC *Question Time* and also a dance with the Acker Bilk Band, supported by the Severnside Jazz Band.

The Company made awards for loyalty by giving staff who had completed ten years of service a pin, and those who had achieved twenty-five years, a special watch.

Regular presentations were made in the canteen at awards celebrations.

Plate 89

Long-service Awards Celebration   Family Archive

Because the Company treated the staff with affection and respect they got it back in spades; it was that kind of Company. The working conditions were excellent.

We had a professional nurse with her own surgery on the premises. This really was a company that cared about the people, whether it was because of the bad experiences which they had had in Germany, I know that George Lobbenberg ran the Company in Harlescott in the 50s and 60s without any kind of rod of iron. I only know this Company was run with a benevolence which you wouldn't have found in many others then, and there would be even fewer today.

It wasn't difficult really. I applied myself with the same sort of enthusiasm, as was evident with the other managers. If you had some business experience, some knowhow, and a reasonably good education, which I had from the Priory Girls School, it wasn't difficult to see where the potential was.

Plate 90

Shipping Department   Adrian Maiden
                                        West Midlands Photo Services

I had started off leading a team of packers and I was quite happy to do this - it was fun and all the girls were great. I didn't have to crack the whip to get them into shape. We just hit on a way of doing things, which I suppose was an informal system of works study.

Instead of each girl packing or folding garments into a box, we organised a packing line: items were progressed, starting with a folder, who passed to a packer, who passed to a labeller, who passed it on to the final packer, who put the item into the box.

After a while, looking after the packing department, I was stopped on the factory floor and asked to go into the office to discuss another job. I didn't really want to go in but was persuaded to do so and, out of the blue, I was put in charge of receiving the orders. Orders were handled at the factory at the time and all the administration was done at Harlescott.

Plate 91

Iris Mills   Iris Mills Archive

The entire administration was run by a handful of people: the production office was the domain of Reg Harrison; the buying department was looked after by Bert Spring and Annemarie and Pamela headed up the design department.

So we did all the ordering, administration, production, buying, design, and looked after welfare. If anything needed doing we did it.

Then sadly we sold out to a Company called Pawsons, quite unexpectedly. Mr Stanley Woodcliff became the new owner of

Silhouette and all of the freehold property that the Company had acquired over the years.

One of the first things the new management team investigated was why stocks were building up to such very high levels. The various functions we as the administrators did were then moved to Leeds.

I suppose it coincided with a lot of other things happening. I can remember that earlier in the seventies we had a reduction in working because of the famous three-day week and then the introduction of the minimum wage and other restrictions on what could be done.

Companies had begun to outsource production, realising that the same things could be made for half the price abroad. We had already lost the M&S contracts because the new management team would not agree to hold stock for customers based on their promises: They wanted order cover and a signed contract.

Our strength was our size and the volumes we could make by the 100 dozen. We had a wide range ready so that when customers ordered we could deliver ex-stock.

The factory had not stopped completely but the only machinists that were working were those with whom we had specific orders; we were not adding to stock.

A lot of girls couldn't understand why, if our swimwear was on sale everywhere, they couldn't make more of it. The sales force which had once covered the country had been disbanded, and if you don't get the orders in, then there is no reason to keep adding to stocks.

Pawsons were running us from Leeds. I remember I went there once with Pam Turner and we were congratulated on how well we were coping with the Company but we felt we were on a downward spiral.
It appeared to us they were slowly selling us off bit by bit, in fact asset - stripping the Company.

Gradually production slowed to such a low level that there were always a few girls leaving us, a few more each week. Several of the girls went to other companies like Laura Ashley and a few went to work for Les Brown at Sylvia Leslie, but gradually production slowly expired.

Sadly not all the skilled machinists got jobs, so they had to change careers. The girls in the offices mostly found other work.

The administration had gone to Pawsons and wages payments were coming from there.

There wasn't any great leaving party because of the gradual decline. I don't think anybody felt particularly sad about it because we were not working for the original families anymore. We were working for Pawsons.

I remember that after the last machinist left Ray Adams was still there. He was responsible for getting the machines and the conveyors dismantled and then moved out. The remaining stock had gone up north and the factory was being cleared for the final auction.

Everything that was left was sold off: chairs, tables and the remaining machines and bits of machines and all the things which hadn't already been sold, including the board room furniture.

It was such an enormous building that there were acres of steel shelving. As Ray Adams and I knew where everything was, we were employed by the auctioneers, and they paid our last wages.

SARAH GRIFFITHS
Machinist at Market Drayton, Whitchurch and Harlescott

I started off at Market Drayton in 1964, and after six weeks of training everything had to be spot on. We had free transport to the factory, which was great because previously I had to cycle 4 miles to work. Within a few months I moved to Whitchurch and carried on straight stitching.

When I moved to Whitchurch there were four or five buses going around bringing in the machinists. We had to clock in on arrival and clock out for lunch, and then back in and out in the afternoon.

We didn't have the conveyor belt system. We had to lift the boxes but they were not heavy until you got to the end when they would be full and quite heavy.

Our wages in those days were always paid in cash, after deductions for tax and national insurance.

We had a half-hour lunch break and the canteen was excellent. After lunch we would go off sometimes for a walk.

I left there to get married and then went to Harlescott and heard it was closing down, about four years afterwards, in 1982.

We worked in teams: Dina would do the cup and then pass it on to me when it was done to keep the work flow continuous. We were paid what was called "piece work", and this meant that you were paid for each piece you made. So much had to be done to earn a basic wage so it was your incentive to do the work, as the more you made the more money you were paid.

At Harlescott, I worked on swimwear but we didn't have much work; it came in dribs and drabs only. That made it difficult to make money. It was a lovely factory and there were lots of nice people. I also remember that Lycra materials were really good to work with and made a lovely swimsuit.

I enjoyed being part of a team very much. Eventually they cut down to a half-hour lunch break so we could go early on a Friday, and I used to go shopping. We cycled everywhere in the 1960s. Holidays were taken at the end of July and the beginning of August, and then there were two weeks at Christmas when all the factories shut down.

We never went abroad in those days. We went to Butlin's Holiday Camp at Pwllheli. One year we went to Yorkshire. Not many people went abroad back then due to lack of money, but you were really able to look forward to a break.

A few of us went to work for Les Brown and his wife. They opened a factory making swimwear, Sylvia Leslie. We were given a variety of brands to make and we didn't worry who the customer was; we just did our jobs and did the work that was there to do.

It was sad, really very sad, when Silhouette went.

Plate 92

Machinists on the steps   Di O'Shea
Babs, Cherida, Mary, Brenda, Chris, Joyce, Pam at the back

CORRINE REES nee Fallows
Pattern Grader and model from 1969 to 1978

I was at school in Harlescott and one day I remember when my dad came home from work, he said "I've got you a job". He was one of the electricians for Silhouette and had worked there for many years.

I wanted to go down to London to do an art course, as one of my teachers at school encouraged me to think about doing an arts degree. You can imagine going home at 15 and telling your parents you wanted to go down to London to study art. No fifty per cent of school leavers went to university in those days.

I went for an interview as a trainee pattern grader and I hadn't got a clue as to what it meant and didn't know what it was all about, but I managed to get the job.

Within a week I had started work and discovered that pattern grading was done in the design department; the designer would come up with a new idea for a product and would also have chosen the fabrics and whatever they needed to finish it. The design to be used and the basic cut-out pattern would be handed over to us.

The pattern graders had to first make it fit a standard size 12 and make sure the fit was perfect. Patterns for all the different sizes were made and then the Silhouette girls were found to model each size.

Our first job was to learn to cut straight lines and then we progressed to using bigger shears to cut thicker card without jags or snags before we moved on to massive shears and thick cardboard patterns.

We cut a straight line and it had to be perfect and then we moved on to curves and, of course, they had to be perfect as well. To start with we had odd patterns to learn, and having learned the skill of cutting straight almost forty years ago, even today I cannot bear to see anybody not cut a straight line. I'm obsessive about it even now!

On the second day I was there, I was measured and found I was a standard size 10, and that's how I started modelling, literally on my second day at work.

Plate 93

Corrine Rees modelling a bikini   Shropshire Star

It was down to being trained by Judy who had very long nails and if the card caught she used to throw it back at you, so you learned very quickly how to perfect it.

After a few months I acquired the skills needed to make patterns in all sizes by paying attention and following instructions, and being careful and totally accurate.

I did go London through being employed by Silhouette, thanks to the Company working with Marks and Spencer. My boss took me down to start with; then I went down to do some modelling and to take new products or new lines for M&S. I would leave patterns and designs for them to assess.

I used to love going to London and running in my lunch hour to the main M&S in Baker Street which was the flagship store then. I was buying things that nobody else in Shrewsbury would have seen.

I modelled the first teen bra. I was a bit older than twelve then, but I was a small size and I was told to put my hair in ribbons and look like a twelve-year-old with high bunches of hair. All in the best possible taste!

Everybody got on; they really did. We were in the office but we still integrated with the girls on the factory floor. We needed the girls: we had to find ones to fit all the different sizes of items we made. We would regularly be chatting to them and bringing them into our room to fit the different samples. They were very happy to come and fit for us as they knew they would get a few freebies here and there and we would say:"take it, wear it and we can alter it." So it was never any trouble for them to come and be fitted.

We would ask women from the office on the corner to come in to try on underwear. We would be fitting and adjusting the garments, and imagine our surprise when one day the guy opposite came round with a big box of chocolates and a card saying "thank you for the floor show at Christmas time". We had no idea they could see in!

Most of the women wore Silhouette underwear anyway and we had a seconds shop which sold all sorts. The shop sold items where the elastic was not quite right and lace bits in the wrong place and odd things like that; garments for the customers had to go out perfect, especially to M&S.

M&S had very high standards which had to be followed. We used the same fabric but they demanded tension on stitching and everything had to be just so, with nothing out of place. If girls were working on the M&S line they had to be top notch - the best.

We developed products and designs, and we gave the most experienced and the best girls on our line the products for M&S. We would cut out the fabric and give them the pattern and they would come to us in the cutting room and sometimes say: "I don't think that elastic is going to pull round that curve. It is not going to be right." That would then help us to modify designs; so everyone had an input.

It was like assembling a jigsaw: you knew after a while what would or would not work, especially on a bra pattern when the machinist would mould it together and the tension would have to be right before it finally went on to the factory floor to be mass-produced.

There were all sorts of people working at Silhouette but my manager Judy was my first port of call; she was the head of my department and I learned an awful lot from her.

I remember Joan Heath; she was wonderful. An aunty, granny, and mother of all, she was just a lovely lady. We could go to her with any problems. Some girls even went to Joan at her home; it didn't seem to matter. She was usually in control and a very supportive person but you knew not to cross her; she made sure things were done her way.

Many things got made in the factory in addition to Silhouette products, and those machines were red hot in the lunch hour. Sometimes they worked far harder in the lunch hour.

Each machinist had their own machine, a straight-stitch machine and an overlocker, and they were very particular that those machines were not tampered with. We used to have to beg to use their machines, and they would stand over us to make sure we didn't do anything wrong.

Plate 94

One of the many survivors   Nigel Hinton
Shropshire

We had our own highly skilled machinists, especially at the weekends when there were a lot of outfits made for a Saturday night and most of the major costumes for the social committee shows.

The Company attempted to diversify and we started to make different things such as a leisure wear range, which probably didn't wear too well, and it was certainly not aimed at the people in Shrewsbury. It included long robes to go over swimwear; you would only wear that if you were going abroad or if you were on a yacht, probably. It was very high class stuff and not for the high volume market we were used to.

The fashion had changed - the miniskirt had reduced the demand for stockings, and bras were being burned, so our traditional markets had all but disappeared. There were more people coming into the industry and I don't think our products were cheap enough. We only realised later that there was much more competition.

It was great for us in the design department as we were working on brightly coloured fabrics and new materials which came in, not just stretching Lycra. We were making long skirts and dresses and we even started making bomber jackets for men's wear. We were trying to find other niche markets to ensure to keep all of the machines filled up.

I can remember doing the children's parties; employees' children were given jelly and ice cream. We did a lot for families whilst I was there.

There were some perks at Silhouette in the design department - I didn't buy underwear or swimwear for years, and I have still got my Premium Bonds, but they have not come up yet.

We had one young man in the design department, Rob Pugh, and he took some stick being the only bloke. The girls would tease him to death. He was only young and had begun in the cutting room.

To those of us in the design department, new product promotion was highly important to the Company. We had to be ready to be photographed at very short notice. The press were always after photographs from Silhouette, to be used when there were no big news stories about, and they would come along and grab one of us and say "come along we will do a season's photograph." It was usually cold when they wanted to do a bikini shot and they took us to places like the Quarry and Haughmond Hill.

I left the Company in 1978 to start a family and did not see it through to the end, but it was a great start for me and I was proud to work for the same company as my dad.

Joan Heath

Many people have memories of Joan Heath, the supervisor with a heart of gold. She not only supervised her girls but supported them and saw them through some of their own personal problems. She was thought of as a mum, a big sister or auntie by everyone and she was a one-person social services department for the Company.

Plate 95

Joan Heath at a social event   Shrewsbury Advertizer

Her own life was affected by the loss of her only child and thereafter she adopted many good causes. She raised money for, and was a supporter of, Loppington House. The following article on how she and other employees helped there is taken from Silhouette Express.

Loppington House:

"Most of you have heard of Loppington House, and indeed many of you have very kindly given your time, skills and money towards fetes, collections and raffles for the children living there, but only a few of you have visited the home. We thought it may be of interest to you to tell you a little about the children, the staff and the object of the money collected.

Our first visit to Loppington took place on a cold March afternoon. We had read in a local paper that very few people visited the babies in the Home, and how the matron felt that a few visitors would brighten up the staff and maybe help the children. We agreed to go, not giving it much thought, but felt that a visit could be interesting.

The Home is about 12 miles from Shrewsbury, set in beautiful grounds and approached from the main road by a long, winding drive, edged with trees. The house was large and rambling, surrounded by well-kept lawns, and behind the house was a small lake which was alive with wildlife.

We met Mrs. Harvey, the matron, in the hallway and after introductions she proceeded to show us around the Home. There are seven separate nurseries of different sizes containing nothing but cots. In each cot there lay a child aged between a few months and 12 years. Our first reactions were of sadness, sorrow and pity. Mrs. Harvey gave us a synopsis of each child as we stood around the cot.

We saw children of every colour and creed, badly deformed children and children that looked quite perfect, but at every cot we stopped by, however deformed or ugly the child, they always had one redeeming feature, maybe beautiful hair, or lovely teeth, or clear fresh skin, but they were all blessed with one good feature.

On the journey home we were all very quiet to start with, probably all busy thinking of what we had just seen. There were 108 babies at Loppington (the number only varies slightly for as soon as one child leaves there are two ready to take his place). They were all very well cared for and loved by the staff, but we felt we must help in some small way.

We decided to visit the children fortnightly, on visiting days. Then every child was 'adopted' by an 'auntie' from Silhouette, who would be responsible for remembering birthdays and Christmas, and we also thought a card sent whilst we were on holiday would be appreciated. The children, of course, wouldn't really benefit from this, but the staff would know that somebody somewhere cared about their babies. We helped at sales of work and many of you sent bits and pieces to be sold and made garments et cetera to help swell the funds.

We have held raffles which you have generously given to, and with all the monies collected they have built a beautiful sun lounge, from which the children derive a great deal of benefit as the sun is so good for them. Our main task is taking the children for walks to give them a little fresh air. Mrs. Harvey has provided a fleet of prams for us and every bright, warm Sunday that we visit, the driveway is alive with pram pushers. We all thoroughly enjoy the walks and so do the children.

We can only take out the less severely handicapped as many of them are far happier lying in their cots and some are too badly handicapped to move. We feel these outings are well worthwhile, when at the end of an afternoon out we arrive back with a baby with a tinge of pink in his cheeks.

Some of the children are visited by their own parents and relatives, but many of the children are some long distance from their homes. All the parents we have spoken to are very happy that their children are so well cared for, and most are relieved that a heavy burden has been lifted from them. We find that most parents really want their children at home with them, but couldn't cope with the continual care and attention needed for them.

No child at Loppington House can walk; no child can feed themselves; only one child can talk at all, and all the children are incontinent. So you can see that this adds up to a lot of hard work for the staff.

When you enter the sun lounge there are little tables with a small plaque in each saying that they were presented by the Silhouette Friends of Loppington. We also presented the seating in the lounge, but the children derive the most benefit from the baby relaxers which are used all over the Home; they were a most useful gift from Silhouette.

We hope we shall continue our association with Loppington for a long time to come. We always feel very sad when one of our little charges is moved to another home, but we always know that there are plenty of other babies at Loppington just waiting for an 'auntie'."

Ray Adams
Maintenance Manager 1957-1982

I started in Nov 1957 and was the last person to lock the door in 1982. I reckon that's 25 years' service. I started as a maintenance electrician, and ended up as group maintenance manager of all the factories. Harlescott had opened the year before I joined but I was there when it was expanded and extended. I was also involved in the building of the Market Drayton factory in 1960.

The Company always tried to be up to date and get the best and most efficient equipment. It was high tech as seen by the introduction of material handling equipment, such as the latest stockroom paternoster that moved products around the factory, carrying finished products from the line up to the stockroom and down to despatch for shipment to customers.

We were also responsible for keeping all the sewing machines running, maintaining all the fixtures and fittings in the building and, of course, maintaining the fabric of the buildings; we even had our own full-time window cleaner. Equipment was moved from factory to factory over the weekends to keep production moving.

The Market Drayton factory was a challenge and trouble, with only one pillar in the middle. It had not been well constructed: the roof beams started to bend and we had to take the roof off and replace the central pillar.

The 300 girls who worked there had to be found places at Shrewsbury, Harlescott and Coton Hill and at the chapel opposite the waterworks in Coton Hill. Some of the machinists had to be moved with their machines into Pelwall House. We rebuilt the roof and, according to my records, the factory was out of commission for over 12 months.

Plate 96

The tape drive of the new computer   Family Archive

In Harlescott in 1966 the new computers were lifted in by crane. We had built a special room on the third floor for them. This had to be humidity controlled, heat and air-conditioning controlled. The glass along the front was triple glazed: the environmental requirements were so demanding.

We set up a room to their specifications and they, NCR, installed the hardware. All the cables ran under the floor; these were as thick as your finger and silver-plated. Positioning was vital in the special room which was environmentally controlled.

Very few companies had the room to install a computer in those days. I would say it was the first in Shrewsbury and Shropshire. Its capacity was seen as massive at the time, but very small compared to current laptops. All the data was stored on tapes, with the master tapes kept at another factory in case of fire. It was broken up for scrap in about 1976 and was replaced by some of the early personal computers which were desktop size.

It was not just sewing machines that needed maintenance; there was the 'Test Lab' full of equipment testing raw materials and the testing of finished products. The testers were making sure the quality of the finished products was of a very high standard. When we started making swimwear we had to look at the effect of chlorine and salt on it, and test elastic or Lycra materials, stretching them to destruction.

We had a busy team of up to 40 skilled men and 60 cleaners who were kept constantly busy. They were all very clean factories with cleaners sweeping throughout the day, picking up lint and off-cuts from the floor and paper between the garments. The floors had to be clean because if a garment fell on a dirty floor it was ruined.

We were proud of our fully-equipped modern workshop at each factory which, being built from scratch with the latest equipment, really made a difference. The maintenance staff were specialists, and there were sewing machine mechanics, a handyman and a gardener at each factory. There was lot of weekend work for us to get machinery and lines in place or reorganised and set up for Monday mornings.

As we acquired more factories further afield, we got really busy and at one stage we were so busy I worked 18 months without a day off. We were also expected to turn out at night, and I was on call in case the alarms went off. Some oversensitive smoke detectors meant many wasted calls, but we had to beat the fire brigade to stop them smashing the doors down!

However, there was a big fire towards the end, when a store room burnt down in September 1979. There were lots of spare machines stored in there and they burned in the fire that was caused by a spark from an arc welder that got into the paper and cardboard. The heat twisted the 6" square girders. Flames touched the new canteen next door. I think at that stage the Company was quite happy to have the insurance money.

It was not all work. The sports and the good social scenes were very important. It was known that applicants for jobs who were good tradesmen were chosen if they could play cricket or football and would be able to play for a Company team. We travelled all over. I remember once the cricket team stopped at Gretna Green on the way to play at Paisley. At Market Drayton there was a big playing field behind the factory for home matches.

The ratio of women to men was about 20 to 1, so all of my apprentices married Silhouette girls, and I went to all of their weddings.

I remember waiting at the level crossing at Harlescott for about 7 minutes in the lunch-break: the road was very busy as girls on bicycles knocked off for their break. Eventually the bike stands were replaced and we had to build a second car park as the women earned enough to buy cars.

The maintenance team in the workshop had lots to do. On various days throughout the year we made go-carts for the fair day. Approximately 300 children were bussed in from other factories at Christmas time;

there were presents for every one of them and various entertainments. There were lots of games and some fights, Punch and Judy, a clown and, of course, goodie bags to take home. The kids' parties always had a theme, for example Snow White and the Seven Dwarfs; once we built a Chitty Chitty Bang Bang.

There was lots of fun; when we built a sleigh we thought we could do with some reindeer so we would send a driver to Attingham Park to get some - plenty there. We got the general manager to send him with some rope. We said we had rung the game keeper and we wrote the order out. He fell for it and we had to stop him going there!

At Christmas the girls got a box of chocolates; men got 100 cigarettes; we all received £2 Premium Bonds for each year worked. The factory closed over Christmas and the New Year, so we all got two weeks` money. Many people received Ten - and Twenty-year service pins, and for Twenty-Five years' service a watch of their choice. Mine is still keeping good time.

It was very sad in the end. Pawsons had taken the Company over and they started stripping the assets. I had the worst job of my life, reducing staff as factories closed. I had to make people redundant; these were grown men with families. It really knocked me about to dismantle my team that I had built up over twenty-five years.

The receivers were busy as they were closing down the engineering factory behind us as well. Pawsons had sold the factory before it was closed down. In the last few weeks everything was sold off. In the last couple of weeks I was clearing up by myself.

On the last day I handed the key to the receiver and left.

Part Eight – The End

In 1979 Chairman Tom Blumenau, a major shareholder then aged 52, met a life guru who asked him if he was happy to continue to do what he had been doing for the previous 33 years.

Tom considered this, and then, after a great deal of thought and soul-searching, went ahead and looked for an alternative lifestyle. He also began looking for a company to take over the running of Silhouette.

The next generation of the Lobbenberg and Blumenau families had started their own careers away from the business, and there was very little chance they would be interested in getting involved with running the Company in future.

Tom felt his main responsibility was to ensure continued employment for the workforce. He thought that, as he was the last connection with the Lobbenberg and the Blumenau founders of Silhouette, it was up to him to decide what to do. He did not consult his fellow board members when he decided to sell.

Tom found Pawsons, a dress-manufacturing company, and arrangements were made for a takeover. Part of the deal included undertakings about continuing employment for the people working in Shropshire.

Pawsons had borrowed money to fund the takeover and within six months of the 1979 election, won by Margaret Thatcher, interest rates peaked at an all time high; the commercial rate was 17%. This was an unexpected additional expense for them.

The new owners did not want to listen to any advice and quickly started disposing of the assets that had been built up over the years.

The undertakings about the people were ignored and the business was stripped of its assets and sold.

Postscript

The phoenix arises from the ashes several times.

The Company changed hands several times before being bought by M.T.M in 1981. M.T.M. owned Spencer, an established company known particularly for their made-to-measure corsetry, and they recognised that the fashionable Silhouette brand would complement Spencer's more traditional product. Silhouette production was transferred to the Spencer factory in Banbury.

In 1984, things changed again, after Silhouette/Spencer underwent a management buy-out. It was recognized that such a relatively small company could not compete directly with the giants of the body fashion industry and a decision was made to target niche markets.

In 1989, Silhouette was bought by Remploy and became part of the newly formed Textile Group. After Remploy decided to withdraw from lingerie manufacturing, Silhouette was bought by a group of private investors who continued the business as Silhouette Ltd.

As a result of the spiralling cost of manufacturing in the UK, Silhouette Ltd went into liquidation in December 2003, but in January 2004, Silhouette Lingerie Ltd bought the designs, machinery and intellectual property rights from the administrators for Silhouette. It continues today to produce high quality lingerie items, including the popular Silhouette brands Cascade, Euphoria, Paysanne, and the Madame X and 'Little X' control garments.

In Shrewsbury life goes on, with the memories of Silhouette still very much in the minds of the people who worked there; there are still echoes of the Company in the buildings that remain.

Plate 97

The interior at Tankerville St in 2009   Nigel Hinton

The original factory on Tankerville Street has been reinstated to its original use and is being used as a church. The old waterworks has become an eco-friendly office complex occupied by businesses including the Wrexham, Shropshire and Marylebone Railway Company and the Marches Energy Agency.

The main factory at Harlescott is currently used by BT. The hyperbolic paraboloid roof has gone from Market Drayton, and Pelwall House is in need of complete renovation.

Silhouette products are still available at specialist shops and, of course, the internet has more or less replaced mail order. The latest generation of customers is buying the products as fashion and leisure wear items.

Silhouette 2009 - The Shape of Things to Come

If ever an organisation epitomised the concept of successful re-invention, it has to be Silhouette. As we have seen, the brand has survived two World Wars, a few financial collapses, several international relocations, several takeovers and a management buyout.

The present owner of the production rights is Silhouette England. Operating out of premises in Manchester with a new team, it is headed by Aras Gasiunas, and supported by Nemira Gasiunas on marketing.

The Company is keen to maintain the link with the past whilst keeping up with, and sometimes setting, trends and new styles in the future. In 2009 sales and marketing is headed by Amanda Joynt, an honours graduate in Textile Design.

The present range will be familiar to many people who have known Silhouette products over the years and the three essential priorities for a good bra are the three priorities we have read about in the earlier chapters: the Fit; the Fit; the Fit.

The present owners bought the equipment and stock from the receiver and now trade under the brand name Silhouette England.

Aras Gasiunas re-engineered Silhouette England as part of a programme he instituted that was run by Nottingham Trent University to enable the key staff and managers to become more involved in the decision-making. This resulted in production going to Europe,

The Company found it difficult to compete against larger companies with extensive fashion ranges and started to specialise in niche products: large and small cup sizes, bridal designs and corsetry. A lot of effort was put in to strengthen these niche product ranges - improving fit - increasing sizes - bridging size breaks and so on, giving the very strong products that are currently being made and sold. This has been a familiar story in the Silhouette experience since its foundation.

Plate 98

The catalogue is available from Silhouette England: 0161 4455863
www.silhouettelingerie.co.uk

Little X today

Plate 99

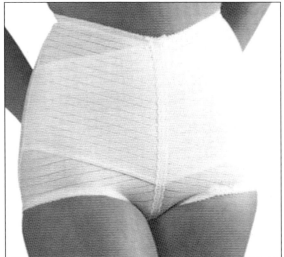

XN6 Pantie Girdle   Silhouette England

Plate 100

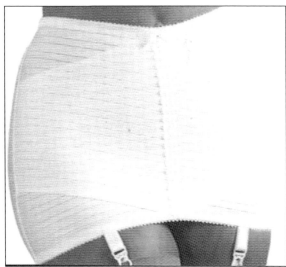

XN1 Open Girdle   Silhouette England

Silhouette - the Musical Play

The story of Silhouette is compelling, and as I speak to more people it is clear that this has been, and, in the memory still is, a very important company to the people of Shropshire. Although the business closed in 1982, there are still many people interested in Silhouette.

Plate 101

Harriet Beechy and Rosie Coxhead   Richard Bishop
Actors in the play

It was whilst watching a performance of *Arthur's Plough*, written by Chris Eldon Lee, that I wondered if a musical play set in the factory in the 1960s would be of any interest to an experienced writer who had written several plays about local events.

I approached Chris and, after he had done some research, we arranged a meeting to discuss the next step. We approached a number of private sponsors and the Arts Council and they agreed to back the project.

It was decided that we should have a coffee morning to give the people who had worked at Silhouette an opportunity to come along and tell us their stories.

Over one hundred and twenty people came along and we were able to record their stories as they met old friends and former colleagues; the nostalgia flowed.

It is on these stories that the play is based, set in the context of a Silhouette factory somewhere in Shropshire, and using music of the 1960s that the people remembered as their favourites.

The play has sold out the eight performances in November 2009 Market Drayton and Shrewsbury and will be rerun in Shrewsbury in March 2010 at Theatre Severn.

The play was sponsored by The Arts Council, Shropshire Council, Andrews Orme & Hinton Ltd, Chartered Accountants, Wace Morgan Solicitors, Marches Care and Darwin Direct Insurance.

Plate 102

Flyer for the play
Design: Mike Ashton

Plate 103

Judy Roberts at Market Drayton Lido   John Rea

A Final Reminder of Silhouette

Evensongs
for
Hekate

Sara Croft
Wicket Icons

Table of Contents

Dedication

It has been a circuitous path to Hekate's service for me. I began studying the typical book version of Wicca and Greek mythology, but I migrated away from the Hellenic Gods through an interest in my ancestor's beliefs, which originated in western Europe. I've gone as far afield as ancient Egypt in my exploration of the mystical in my life.

But the journey began with Hekate, and to Her I returned. Today, I believe that it will be the Torchbearing Goddess who will guide me past the Gates of Mystery at death. I have my moments of doubt, of course. Those who say otherwise aren't being honest with themselves. This book is a culmination of more than a decade of dedicated practice in Hekate's service. There are many to whom I owe gratitude in my work with Hekate, and in the time I have spent on this book. My husband, Tina, Maggie and Matthew, Jennifer, Justine, Sorita, Florian, and many others spring to mind. Without all of you, my many works dedicated to Hekate would not exist today. Thank you all.

And, of course, to Hekate Herself, who has haunted and urged and pushed me to be a better person as well as a more effective devotee over these years.

Hekate: Liminal Goddess

The Goddess Hekate has had something of a renaissance among polytheists in recent years, so I will forgo an in depth explanation of Her history and myths. In the appendix, you will find some insights into Her symbols, holidays, etc. For an in depth treatment from a Pagan perspective, I heartily recommend the writings of Jason Miller, Mat Auryn, Cyndi Brannen, Sorita D'Este, and the academic works of Sarah Iles Johnston and Daniel Ogden.

Hekate originated somewhere in either Caria (in modern day Turkey) or in Thrace (modern day Bulgaria), near as we can tell. Her earliest appearance in Hesiod's *Theogony* presents a youthful yet powerful Goddess with wide-ranging authority over many aspects of life. In the Homeric Hymns, Hekate helps Demeter find out about the fate of Her daughter after the God of the Underworld abducted Persephone. Over time, Her chthonic nature came to prominence, and She became associated with ghosts, phantasms, and witchcraft. Finally, in late antiquity, the Chaldean Oracles understood Hekate to be a vast and nearly omnipotent Goddess who was the origin of both the Soul and the virtues of faith, truth, and love.

Today, Hekate is honored by witches, Hellenic reconstructionists, Wiccans, and many other practitioners of magic.

Introduction to Hekate

In writing about ancient beliefs and their modern counterparts, there are a few things to keep in mind. Building a tradition off the surviving documents, art, and archaeology is a piecemeal process, and interpretations vary, even amongst scholars. There are gaps in what we know about the ancient world, in spite of the emphasis that the Western World has always placed upon Greece and Rome. Much of what we know about ancient Greece comes from Athens, and the surviving tidbits of information from other areas allow us to understand that each region approached the Gods with similarities of general practice and differences in terms of belief and detail. Additionally, the practices and beliefs of the ancient world as to the nature of the world and the divine were not static. Those beliefs and practices changed over time, in a natural progression, as their societies grew.

Further, there are aspects of ancient society that I have no desire to resurrect. It was, in the main, a severely patriarchal world, with few opportunities for women, and an ambivalent relationship with magic, in which people both sought and decried witchcraft.

My aim in writing this book is to be accessible by those new to Hekate, but an understanding of contemporary Paganism and polytheism is handy to understand the rituals and practices explored herein.

Hekate has had a long existence and Her praxis spans a vast range of both time and regions. This book includes both the gentle and near-omnipotent Titaness of Hesiod and the Fearsome Goddess leading the Furies and Restless Ghosts of the past. It also celebrates the vast spiritual fire of the Chaldean Hekate.

The book is divided according to content. First I will share how I connect with Hekate, including a version of the ritual I did to introduce myself to Her, and the rituals I enact daily or as needed in my personal practice. Not all of these practices are Hellenic or Reconstructionist.

My own spiritual journey began in a solidly Wiccan methodology, and though my path has meandered through several other traditions, there remains an element of Wicca in my practice. In my thirty years of work, a certain amount of deviation is to be expected. Forgive the audacity.
I am certain that what I have shared here won't work for everyone, and may even oppose your personal experiences and insights. There is nothing wrong with that. Hekate is a Goddess who has been described as gentle and fierce, kind and cruel, and our meager attempts to experience Her will deviate according to our own needs, experiences, and the specifics of our relationship with Her. I am not the sole nor the greatest authority on the Threefold Goddess, and another Hekatean might be a better match for your own path.

Some of the hymns, poems, and prayers I share in this book are ultimately informed by UPG, Unverified Personal Gnosis. This does not invalidate any meaning for me, but it does mean that it might not be totally backed with a historical source. Most of it, however, has at its root, some element of the history we know of Hekate and Her associates. I study the history, culture, and philosophy of the cultures over whom Hekate had influence to act as a counter-balance to the possibility of my own ego or wishful thinking misleading my practice. To that end, I highly recommend picking up copies of The Homeric Hymns and Hesiod's Theogony to at least have a grasp on the way that the Greeks initially understood Her.

If something here doesn't resonate with your own experiences, take it as an opportunity to develop your own path. Get to know the Gods yourself, but also recognize that you can say no to the Gods and the other practitioners.
Your path is just that, yours. You have the authority and the power, and Hekate of all the Gods would be the first to tell you to claim your unique journey. Come to your own insights and conclusions.

Is Hekate the mysterious Goddess that empowers the plots of Shakespeare's witches? Is She the guide of kings, sailors, fishers, athletes, and shepherds as Hesiod tells? Or is she the being responsible for the creation of your very soul, and the virtues that gives life its weight? Could it be she is all that and more? Each of us will have our own unique experience with Her, influenced by our lives, by our approach to Her, and by what we ask and need in our day to day.

My hope is, whether you remain with Hekate or move elsewhere on your own journey, to give you some tools and knowledge to develop a relationship with her.

Who is Hekate?

Reading The Homeric Hymn to Demeter, we encounter an image of Hekate who has compassion when others kept silent. She leads Demeter towards answers as to the fate of Her daughter, Persephone, who has been abducted by Hades. In some versions of the story, Hekate even goes out of Her way to cheer Demeter. And in the end, Hekate becomes the constant companion to Persephone and one of those who guides Her between the realms.

She is described as three-faced[1], or three-formed. She is the ever-young maiden. Her earliest depictions are beneficient, focused around childbirth and light-bringing, with a gentle and compassionate nature. By the fifth century, She is the patron of Medea, powerful in herbcraft, of poisons and spells. Centuries later, in The Chaldean Oracles, She is the Goddess that Ensouls the World, the Tree of Life, and the source of virtue and creation.

It is Hekate who leads us beyond boundaries. As a guide, she is challenging or gentle, as need requires. In my own life, She is a light in the darkness. Her torches light the path ahead, illuminating the realities of my own decisions.

---

[1] Her earliest figure is singular, however, and her threefold nature is first credited to Alkamenes by Pausanias. There are also four-figure Hekate icons found occasionally.

She is Kourotrophos[2], the child nurse, who eases childbirth and helps children. She is the Torchbearer (Dadophoros) and Lightbringer (Phosphoros). She is the daughter of Asteria, a Titaness of the Stars, and Perses, who is a Titan associated with War. Sappho said that Hekate serves Aphrodite as a handmaiden. She is also Hekate Enodia, the Goddess of the Road.

Her greatest sanctuary is in modern day Turkey, in an area that was once known as Karia. The Sanctuary at Lagina, what survives today, is a Hellenistic site, but the examination of the site suggests that it has a long history. There, Hekate had close ties with Zeus, and was associated with keys. But Her worship was known throughout the Mediterranean.

It is Hekate who can lead us each through our most harrowing moments, and many of us found our relationship with Her when we were transitioning through difficulties and struggling to survive. She is a guide when She carries us after death, and She is our guide when we are born into a new life. For me, it has been Hekate Hegemonen (Guide) who meets me where I am, and shows me where I could be. It is up to me to make the leap and take the risk.

As the Goddess of crossroads and boundaries, She is defined by liminality, by all things that are between. Hekate is the torchbearer, guiding us through the darkness, and the keybearer who unlocks Mysteries. She also guards the home from outside influence. As Hesiod's glowing description says:

---

[2] In the appendix, some of the most common epithets and their meanings are listed.

She receives honours also in starry heaven, and is honoured exceedingly by the deathless Gods.

...

Great honour comes full easily to him whose prayers the Goddess receives favourably, and She bestows wealth upon him; for the power surely is with Her.[3]

In Her Many Names, may Her fires shine bright upon your path.

[3] Hesiod, *The Theogony*, line 414 and 429-430. Translation by Evelyn-White, *H.G. Loeb Classical Library*, vol. 57, London, 1914.

Chapter 2:

Rituals

After learning what you can about Hekate via books, nothing is better than getting in there and doing the work! If you have any experience with witchcraft or Paganism as it exists today, you probably have done similar activities. I am a fan of fairly simple rituals, so you won't find anything that requires rare ingredients or elaborate and expensive tools.

Preparations

Before every ritual that I dedicate to Hekate, I have a set of rituals that I enact. Developing a set of actions will go far to shape a healthy relationship with any of the Gods. It is ultimately something you will have to create on your own, but here is how I begin my practices.

First, I bathe. This may include candlelight, music, bath salts, herbs, and oils. Do any of this with intention, and try to include symbols of the deity you are approaching. In this case, Hekate. I suggest using caution when picking out plants associated with Her. After all, She's closely associated with some of the most potent poisons found in nature.

Suggested herbs: myrrh, bay laurel, amber, juniper, cypress, lavender, rosemary, jasmine, poppy, pomegranate, or saffron.

This is far from an exhaustive list, and I have not mentioned the toxic substances. As tempting as it might be while lounging in the bath, I don't recommend wine or any other mind altering substances here. Leave behind the worries of the day, and take some time to just be. Sometimes I meditate in the bath, using Hekate's name as a focus.

You want to come out of the bath feeling refreshed, centered, and clear. Most of all, focused. I then take my ritual oil (recipe in the appendix), and anoint myself. I take a drop of oil and place it in six places on my person, while reciting the following:

Blessed be my feet that walk upon the Path.
Blessed be my knees that kneel before the Gods.
Blessed be my seed from whence creation springs.
Blessed by my heart within which my soul does sing.
Blessed be my voice which speaks the Sacred Names.
Blessed be my mind which seeks the Mysteries.

I use seed instead of gendered language like womb/phallus, even though that's more traditional in contemporary Witchcraft. Those of you who know the process of initiation and the Great Rite in some traditions of Witchery will recognize the origin of some of the language here.
Dress in clean, appropriate clothing. Choose things that make you feel good, are comfortable, and won't leave you encumbered or struggling to keep your sleeves out of the candle's fires.

That's it! I then proceed to set up my altar and do the ritual I have planned.

A Rite of Introduction

Before enacting this ritual, read up on Hekate. The Theoi.com site is ideal for this kind of study. Based on what you read, choose a few symbols. It doesn't have to be anything fancy, and you don't need to go overboard. It is possible that you'll want to do this rite multiple times, as a means of encouraging the connection. A candle is ideal. It is also possible that you'll have indications that this is not what you should be doing right now, and it would be a shame to spend a lot of time, money, and energy only to hear no. You will want a journal or other place to record your thoughts.

Ideas for symbols for this ritual:

Draw a key on a piece of paper, light a candle, use a tarot card that has art that makes you think of Hekate, or a flower. Incense is useful, as are stones that make you think of her. You can even focus on Hekate's name. You'll find a short list of offerings and symbols in the appendix.

Write a short prayer or hymn. Put it in your journal. You can use one of the ones in this book, but you'll have better luck by writing it personally. Follow your intuition, and remember, you are just introducing yourself.

Time this ritual to be done at the dark or new moon. The full moon can also suffice. Liminal times, such as dawn, dusk, or midnight are preferred.

Take a shower and allow all the tensions and worries of the day to be washed away. Put on clean clothes that make you feel good. If you like, dress in Hekate's colors: red, black, white, saffron orange, or yellow.

Set up a space where you will be in solitude or at least be undisturbed for a time. Place your chosen symbol before you, with any additional tools or images. Take a deep breath and double check that you have all that you need. If you're using a candle or incense, do you have a lighter or matches?

When all is prepared, if you have a practice that establishes sacred space, this is the time to do so.

Light your candle, and focus on your symbol. Take three deep breaths, and be still. Offer up your written prayer. Introduce yourself, and explain why you are there. Then sit still and listen.

Take your time. Pay attention to your feelings and thoughts. How long you sit and connect is up to you. In short, meditate and pray.

Hekate has been known to express Her presence with flickering candles, pressure in the room, an indescribable shift in atmosphere, or, most historically, dogs barking in the distance.

When you feel like you've gotten all you can from the meditation, express your gratitude. How you choose to do so will likely be determined by what you felt as a response.

If you have established sacred space, finish out the rite accordingly. Now record your experience in a journal or even on your computer. It might not, indeed, likely won't, be a huge change in your spiritual life instantly. Make notes of anything you need to change or do differently, and whether you want to do the rite again. That night, pay attention to your dreams, and for days afterward, pay attention to your day to day life for things related to Hekate.

If you did not get a clear response or any reaction at all, don't fret. This may need to be done more than once. If you received a clear no, don't worry. It might not be the right time, and Hekate may come to you later. It might be that this isn't the right path for you. Neither are a comment on your worthiness as a person or as a devotee. This is not a path for everyone. With luck, dedication, and a little perseverance, this ritual can begin a relationship with the Goddess of Three Ways.

Torches for Hekate

I keep two candles in my shrine at all times, dedicated to Hekate Dadophoros in Her role as a Guide in my spiritual life. They are the Torches that Hekate holds aloft in good times and bad, and are one of my favorite tools.
The ritual is best enacted on the New Moon.

You will need:

2 candles (I recommend soy or beeswax, with lead free wicks)

A bowl of water

1 bay leaf

Candleholders

A tool for carving the candles (I sometimes use dead pens, sometimes knives.)

Lighter or matches

Using the lighter or matches, catch the leaf on fire and quench it in the water, saying:

I purify and bless this water in the names of all the Gods.

I carefully wipe down the wax of the candle with the water, careful to avoid the wick. Envision the wax being purified and blessed.

Carve Hekate's name into the candle. I usually write it in Greek, but you may choose to write it as you wish. As you carve, see the candles being held as torches in Hekate's hands.

Hold that image in your mind. Chant Hekate's name under your breath while you work. Place the torches in their candleholders, which will now be dedicated to this purpose. Position them in a prominent position on your altar or in a special place in your home.

As always, write down your response to the ritual, and keep notes on how the candles affect the altar. Use them until they are burned down, and replace them with new candles also blessed to be Hekate's torches.

Blessing the Home

While cleaning your home is an integral part of the Deipnon[4] done at the Dark Moon, sometimes life calls for something more. This ritual cleansing and protection spell has served me well when life was feeling particularly rocky. Not only does it leave you with a home that feels more peaceful, but any crossed energies surrounding you and yours will be protected against once this is finished.

Start by doing a thorough cleaning of your home. If need be, corral family and friends into helping you. It's a good time to rearrange furniture, or purge your life of those things that have outlived their usefulness and importance with you.

For the Cleansing, you'll need:

Bay leaf   candle
salt water (sea water is best, but adding three or nine pinches of salt to water works)
A lighter   Your altar
a simple offering (I tend to use a bulb of garlic for this)
A sigil or symbol of protection (your choice! I do pentacles or key symbols)

For the Blessing and Protection, you'll need:
Incense associated with blessing (I like rosewood and amber.)
The candle you lit for the cleansing.

---

[4] The Deipnon, Hekate's Suppers, are rituals of cleansing and home blessing that the ancient Greeks performed every Dark Moon. See Appendix C.

Prepare your water by dissolving the salt in it, if you aren't using sea water. At your altar, say:

Hail to the Gods of my household, and Hail to the Goddess of Three Ways,
Hekate
Hekate
Hekate
Hail to the Ancestors, and to the daemones[5] who watch over my days,
Accept this simple offering and bless the rite,
Let the water be pure, Let it pour forth upon all that is mine, Let it bring purity to all it touches.

Light the candle. Set the bay leaf aflame, and speak:

By the sacred plant, let the water be blessed!

Put the burning leaf in the water, quenching the flame. This is how I make khernips, a water for ritual purification, that is used in many Hellenic rituals.

Anoint yourself with the water, feeling the purification flow over you and those who are part of your household.

Now, take the water to your front door, and walk counter-clockwise through your house, sprinkling the lustral water along the boundary of each room and then the center of it. Stop at each window, exit, and mirror, and mark them with the protective sigil using the water.

---

[5] Daemones, or daimones, are spirits in Hellenic practice. Socrates famously credited his wisdom as being from listening to his personal daimon. The word is the root of the English word demon, though the original Greek carried no implication of good or evil in and of itself. Rather there were agathos daimones (good spirits) and kakodaimones (evil spirits).

Continue until you are back to your front door. This can take a good amount of time, but it's worth it. At the front door, if possible, toss the last of the water out the door, visualizing all the heavy energy that you're removing from the space leaving with it. Close your door firmly, and return to the altar.

Light the incense on the candle, and say:

Accept this offering of sweet incense, Gods of my Home! May it be a blessing upon us!

Starting at the front door, carry the incense clockwise through the home, following the boundary of each room, and wafting the scent around. After you return to the door, take the incense back to the altar.

Take up the candle, and hold it carefully, while you say:

Let the fires of our household be warm and bright,
Let the fires of our hearts be guarded, as the fires kept the wolves at bay for our ancestors,
Let the fires be a warning to those who would oppose us.

Carry the candle carefully to each door, window, and mirror in the house, and visualize the firelight being captured by them, held there as a boundary against all ill things. Any trouble which may approach your property or person will find their will burned away.

Return the candle to the altar, and offer your thanks to those beings who have witnessed and given your rite their own boost. Gratitude is best offered in a way that is personalized. Carefully close out your rite. I let the candle burn down with the incense, and take this as an opportunity to pray or meditate.

Close out the ritual as you prefer.

If you want, you may also wish to extend the ritual into your yard. I wouldn't necessarily do the purification, but the blessing and protection can be easily personalized. I like to take stones, bless them, and paint them with a protective sigil, and bury them at the corners of the yard. Other options are to plant protective plants, or to create a witch bottle and bury it in the yard.

Rite of Three Keys

This is a month-long ritual that creates three keys for use in a wide range of purposes. The first ritual happens at the New Moon. The second at the Full Moon. The third is at the Dark Moon. While complex, the end result are three keys attuned to the three realms over which Hekate has dominion: Heaven, Earth, and Sea. Take your time gathering your supplies.

You'll need:
Three Keys, each of a unique character. My own are brass, bronze, and silver, but choose according to your own tastes and intuitions. Each should reflect something of Heaven, Earth, or Sea.

New Moon necessities:

The Key for Heaven
Solar or angelic incense (I like rosemary, cinnamon, or poppy)
White or yellow candle
Solar or angelic oil for anointing the candle
Things that make you think of stars and sun and the sky.
Offerings that are bright, light, or otherwise associated with the sky.

Full Moon necessities:

The Key for the Sea
Ocean or watery incense (I like mint, jasmine, or amber)
Blue or black candle
Ocean or watery oil for anointing the candle
Things that make you think of lakes, the ocean, and the deep darkness of the water.
Offerings associated with the sea or water.

Dark Moon necessities:

The Key for the Earth
Ancestral or earthy incense (I like dragon's blood, or juniper)
Red or black candle
Ancestral or earthy oil for anointing the candle
Things that make you think of death, earth, and the mysteries of the afterlife.
Offerings associated with the earth or ancestors.

The preparations are largely the same for all three rituals. Clean your house. Take a ritual bath or shower to prepare, and dress in colors associated with each realm. Set up your altar, and take some time to meditate on each realm. When you are prepared, anoint the candle with the oil, visualizing the energies you sensed during your meditation filling the candle completely.

Now establish your sacred space as you prefer.

For the New Moon, invoke Hekate Ourania:

Khaire[6] Hekate Ourania!
Daughter of Stars,
Honored by Zeus,
Beloved by Helios!
In your many names, I beseech you
Turn your gaze upon this rite,
To accept these offerings,
And send down your heavenly servants to aid me!

For the Full Moon, invoke Hekate Einalia:
Khaire Hekate Einalia!
Horse-Headed Mistress,
Beloved of Poseidon,
Mother of Skylla!
In your many names, I beseech you
Turn your gaze upon this rite,
To accept these offerings,
And send forth your waterborn servants to aid me!

For the Dark Moon, invoke Hekate Chthonia:

---

[6] Khaire is a transliteration of the Greek word *Χαῖρε* which was used historically as a greeting. It is roughly equivalent to saying 'Welcome!' or 'Be of good cheer!'

Khaire Hekate Chthonia!
Soul-walker who wanders near and far,
Companion to Persephone,
Protectress of the Outcast and Restless Dead,
In your many names, I beseech you
Turn your gaze upon this rite,
To accept these offerings,
And send forth your earthy servants to aid me!

After invoking the Goddess, as you mention the servants joining the ritual, light the candle that you have prepared.

May the Company of Hekate bless this candle that it be an extension of their powers and subject to my Will.

Visualize the energies of the daemones of Hekate coalescing in the flame.

Take up the key, speaking:

As Hekate carries the Keys to the Cosmos, so I name you, Key to the Powers of Heaven (Sea/Earth), that you be empowered as a bond and as a source of that connection. In the names of Hekate Ourania (Einalia/Chthonia), so it is!

Anoint the key, and visualize the relevant power being bound to the item. In your mind's eye, it should embody the realm's energy for you.

So it is bound, a symbol and watch for my Path, oh Hekate Enodia, a servant to Your Will, my Goddess.

Offer up your offerings, give Her all your gratitude, and thank the daemones that have helped you. Be sure to send them back to their natural realm.

Close out your ritual as is your custom, and clean up. Keep the candles to recharge the keys in the future should the need arise.

I have used my copies of these keys to connect quickly with a particular aspect of Hekate, to remind myself of some ideal associated with Hekate, and to help establish ritual altars dedicated to particular energies associated with the Heaven, Earth, and Sea. They can be worked into jewelry, but I keep mine in a special place in my altar, and are always the final step to re-establishing my shrine during cleaning.

The Charge of the Ineffable Goddess

In Wicca, the Charge of the Goddess is a ritual document used as part of the most sacred rituals they can enact. In my own practice, I have generally treated it more as a theological document. Doreen Valiente's *The Charge of the Goddess* is one of my favorite spiritual poems, and I would be a fool to think that my own meager offering is anything approaching that insight. Nonetheless, I have used this verse with great results in my devotionals. Perhaps some of you might find inspiration to create your own, or elicit some contemplations as to the nature of the Divine, and the Many Gods that we might know.

By flame, by thorn and bloom
By ocean, by glade and desert
By blood, by pain and pleasure
Speak the wisdom of the Ages
Time passes and are but moments for me
Yet I hear each word you speak
Long have I stood and watched you march
The progress of your days.
I am the spark that changes
The flesh that calls your need,
The death that is a door,
The cry of the newborn.
Pound frustrations in my presence,
Sing dirges in my sight,
Tell me of your romance,
Whisper hoarsely of your pains.
I am the mother of creation,
The devourer of worlds,
The child you long to see,
The lover's kiss upon you.
I bring forth Love,
I have taught the pursuit of Truth,
Of Courage, and of Grace.
With honor as your Guide
Cherish the gifts around you,
Embrace the days you see.
Give thanks for every shadow
For they allow you to see.
I am the marrow and the blood,
The heart of all creation.
Embrace me in light and in dark,
Sense my presence at your side.
Along the path of choice
Only you may ride
Act not in hubris,
But pursue your truest Will.

For though these words be truthful
Know this,
Though I am known,
I am ineffable and free.

Meditations

Throughout the world, meditation is used in a variety of ways to connect with the universe. In some cultures, meditation is accomplished through silencing the rambling thoughts that fill our days. Others pray or read in a meditative state. Some repeat phrases. You'll find your own method over time. Sometimes I meditate on long walks, and other times before the altar in the candle light. Here are a few of the phrases that I use to focus as needed.

Hagia Hekate, Hagia Thea
Holy Hekate, Holy Goddess

Hekate Ourania, Hekate Einalia, Hekate Chthonia, Trioditis
Hekate of the Heavens, Hekate of the Sea, Hekate of the Earth, Three-Formed

Hekate, Light my way,
Hekate, Shine Bright!
When I am in darkness, you bring peace.
When I am in darkness, you bring healing.
When I am in darkness, you bring faith.
(Epithet)

Choose the epithets that come to your mind in that moment, and then repeat. You can continue with the same epithet on each rendition, or opt for a different one on each pass. This is my walking meditation.

Pathworking

Meditation comes in many different forms, but one of the most popular for devotional practices has to be Pathworking. Essentially, it's meditation with a script. Some people record their voice reading it; others work them into a group activity with one person reading and the others working through in their mind's eye. You'll need to find a position that is comfortable, where you won't be disturbed. I prefer not to over-complicate the process. I simply find a time and place that works for me, and settle in. Others may set up sacred space, burn incense, and light candles, but having fire when you aren't aware of what's going on around you physically is not safe if you are by yourself. Be practical.

Sometimes it happens that you fall asleep while trying to meditate. Don't stress it. That's just your body tending to its own needs. Try again later when you aren't as sleepy, or change where it is that you're meditating. If you only use your bed for sleep, meditating there is going to be more likely to allow you to drift off.

This first pathworking was originally written for Hekate's Night, a modern Hekatean festival[7], on November 16. It doesn't have to be kept to that timing, however.

---

[7] The appendix includes a section on Hekate's Festivals and times of worship.

Light in the Dark

Settle into a comfortable position. Take three deep calming breaths, and let the pressures of the day slide away for a time. When you feel yourself relaxing, close your eyes and begin.

You are standing upon a dirt track through a meadow. The breeze is soft and carries the smell of fresh earth, and night is beginning to settle across the land. As you follow the track, you feel your body receding from you. You sink deeper, and as you descend, the path winds its way into a forested valley. The sky darkens, filling with stars, and with each step the trees obscure their silvery light. The forest is dark, and full of nighttime whispers – frogs, crickets, owls, quiet things rustle in the underbrush. The path is steady, even. In spite of the darkness, you find that the path is lit around you.
Take a moment to appreciate that light.
You walk through the darkness of the forest, and the air is cooling. Ahead, you see the path splits in two. On one side, the way leaves the valley, rising higher. The other descends deeper. Between them you see an altar to Hekate, lit by torches.
As you approach the altar to pray, you realize you have something in your hand. An offering. You place it upon the altar, and take a moment to honor Hekate.
Having paid your respects, you turn to the lower path, and descend into darkness, certain of the power of your light.
The path takes you deeper, down and down, and the darkness becomes velvety dark. The sounds of the forest fall away, a cave rises before you. This path takes you into the earth herself.
The cave is silent, but for the sound of your footfalls, and the occasional drip of water from the ceiling. The path seems to spiral through the cavern, always steady under your feet.
Slowly ahead you see a light, dimly at first, but growing brighter. And brighter. The air smells of stone and water.
You reach the source of the light. Take your time with it. Allow it to take shape in your mind.

You find another offering in your hand, and leave it in honor of what you have seen. And you turn, following the path back out of the cave, on the path. Carefully, you work your way back into the dark earth, and out, into the forest, which seems loud after the silence of the cave.

You follow the path up, and up, and up. As you walk the path, you begin to feel the weight of your body, slowly you return here, to your home, feel your breath flow in, out. In. Out.

As you return, slowly wiggle your toes and fingers, and when you feel ready, open your eyes.

Immediately record your experiences, making note of how the altar appeared, what gifts you gave, and what you saw in the cave.

In spellwork

Ultimately, Hekate is a witch's Goddess, and incorporating Her guidance into such things can really alter one's practice. A lot of my own spells are bound up in paintings, illustrations, embroidery, and even knitting. The magic is in the colors I choose, the methods I adopt, and even the time I spend working on the piece. It is also in the words I speak while I work.

Hail Hekate,
And bless this work,
I have wrought with my hands,
With my Will,
And with Power.
Let the spell fly true,
Bound to the shape
I have given it,
In keeping with your far-sighted wisdom.
So be it.

And for fabric pieces, I have a verse based on a verse I wrote for a dedication ceremony, something that I firmly believe should be written by the practitioner themselves, unless they are practicing with a group, which will give you guidance as needed.

By my hand, I have woven it.
A devotion wrought in thread.
Knotted, twisting, woven true.
A spell thrice blessed
O Goddess of Threefold Paths,
Keybearer, Torchbearer, Source!
Let each thread stand as a promise
Let my Will be bound herein.
Let the spell be true
In this wondrous rite.

Hymns

Deep in the Forest

Deep in the forest where few dare to tread
There stands a grove of poplars
And there stands a maiden
She waits there for me.
Her torches, they shimmer and shine in the night
Against the darkness of trees.
A growling descends from the hills near and far
When I stand at the crossroads with She.
Deep in the forest where few dare to tread
There stands a grove of poplars
And there stands a maiden
She waits there for me.
She knows all the secrets that I could not speak.
The truth Her torches reveal.
The Mysteries She holds for those who would seek
Span the Heavens, the Earth, and the Sea.
Deep in the forest where few dare to tread
There stands a grove of poplars
And there stands a maiden
She waits there for me.
I pull on my gown,
I let down my hair,
She gives me the key.
I journey the darkness,
Her hounds at my heels,
Her torches are guiding my way.
Deep in the forest where few dare to tread
There stands a grove of poplars
And there stands a maiden
She waits there for me.

Sing

Sing of the far-shooting daughter,
    who stands in strength over all realms.
Sing of the night-wanderer
    with hounds nipping at Her gown.
Sing of the torchbearing queen,
    gentle nurse of the young
    whose mother shines down upon us.
Hekate, at the crossroads in the night,
Queen of the restless,
Guardian of the outcast,
Protectress of women.
I sing your praises between earth and sky.
I sing of the soul walker who leads us through the gate of
Death.
I sing of the Attendant
    who walks with Kore
        who walks with Aphrodite
            who attends all souls.
Hekate, I sing your praises, though it makes my heart pound.

In the Dark

I whisper in the dark,
deep inside,
In the caverns,
In the shadows,
In the spaces,
I fear to go.
Your light washes over me,
The brightness aches my eyes,
Or is it the light-bearing truth that stabs my heart?
The path appears in your light,
The darkness dims.
deep inside,
in the caverns,
in the shadows,
in the spaces,
You shine.

Drakaina[8]

Khaire, Hekate!
You whose hair is coiled with snakes,
You who dress with flaming serpents,
You whose whip flashes forth in fury.
Oh Drakaina!
You who, like the Furies, bring Justice,
You who glides on serpent scales,
You who are known as the Oroboros.
I lift up your names,
I sing your praise,
And offer you my devotions.
Let your kindness warm the hearts of children,
Let your wisdom guide those who follow your light,
Let your grace bless the homes of your devotees.

---

[8] Drakaina: an epithet found in the Greek Magical Papyri that translates as 'serpent' or 'dragon'.

Despoina[9]

Hekate Despoina
Mistress of Heaven, Earth, and Sea.
Your shining crown arrayed with sacred fire,
Your gown of saffron, rich and warm,
Golden, your sandals.
Bright are your torches upon the path
Bringing into vivid clarity the truths of your Mysteries,
You carry the keys that open the center of us all.
Spilling our light and our dark across the temple in stark relief.
Grateful, we lift your many names in song and praise.
Hekate Despoina,
May our devotions serve you well.

---

[9] Despoina: meaning 'Mistress' or 'Lady', this title is applied to most Goddesses at one time or another.

Glory

Khaire Chrysosandalos[10],
Glorious you are, arrayed in white,
Full of power and glory,
Casting light around
In the darkness of the Underworld,
Hekate, you shine,
Upon the path we tread,
And we are blessed to see the road
By your golden torchlight.

Boundless

Hekate Trioditis[11],
Without boundary are you,
Goddess of Souls,
For you are the Anima Mundi[12],
The Source from which we spring,
To whom we flow back upon Death,
We call to you from every land,
Soul to soul,
We seek your holy light,
Mortal moths,
Seeking to be consumed,
In your presence.

---

[10] Chrysosandalos: of Golden Sandals, an epithet found in the PGM, Greek Magical Papyri, a collection of fragmentary spells.

[11] Trioditis: of Three Roads. Hekate's triplicity is well known, as is Her association with roads and boundaries.

[12] Anima Mundi: Latin for Soul of the World. Hekate is often described as such in The Chaldean Oracles.

Mother of Virtues

Khaire, Hekate Chrysostephanos[13]!
Queen, Bright and True!
You shine, your torches bright,
Arrayed in fine gowns and jewels,
Graceful mother of Virtues,
Soteira[14]!
We honor you, Kalliste[15]!

Physis[16]

Hekate Athanatos[17],
Your grace spans all realms,
You are the Source,
And Soul of All.
From you we descend,
Unto you we return,
And our gratitude is poured upon the wide Earth.

---

[13] Chrysostephanos: Golden-crowned, or Crowned with Splendor. This name is given to Hekate, Herakles, and Aphrodite.

[14] Soteira: Savior. For the best exploration of Hekate Soteira, see Sarah Iles Johnston's book of that name.

[15] Kalliste: Fairest. This epithet is best known from the beginning of the Iliad, when Eris interrupts a gathering of the Gods by throwing an apple in their midst with 'For the Fairest' written on it, prompting a debate among the Goddesses, Aphrodite, Athena, and Hera about who was most beautiful.

[16] Physis: Nature. In the Chaldean Oracles in particular, Hekate is understood to be Nature Herself.

[17] Athanatos: without Death, Deathless. An integral trait of the Gods.

Bringer of Light

Hail unto you, Mother of Virtues!
Bringer of Light!
Hekate Soteira,
You are the light which guides,
Burning deep within.
Revealing all with your graces,
Hekate, you tower above your creation,
Welcoming us back into your presence.
The angeloi[18] whisper, cry, and sing
of your beauty and power.
How you stand fast to guard those you Will.
How you bless those within your benevolent gaze when you
Will.
How your absence is as the loss of air and light itself if you
Will it so.
Hekate, you stand between all thresholds, hold all keys, know
all the secret names.
You, first child of the Ineffable, unto you I pray.
That your Will be kind to me and mine.

---

[18] Angeloi are messengers. The Greek word is the root of our word Angel today. Hekate Herself can be called Angela or Angelos historically, in Her role as companion and messenger for Persephone, and rarely, Aphrodite.

Komas[19]

Hekate Komas
I revel in you
How your mysteries deepen
How I find myself
On new paths,
With new insights,
May it always light my way,
This joy I find in you.

---

[19] Komas: Reveler. One of the titles for Hekate in The Chaldean Oracles.

En Erebos, Phos[20]

In darkness, light
In bright day, shade
Hekate the Infinite Ensouler.
In sadness, respite
not flinching away,
forward, through.
In joy, encouragement
Hekate, you stand with torches high,
Above, below, within, without,
You are the principle
the light that shines
within all things.
Hekate, my savior, my queen,
In darkness, you shine.
In light, you are brighter still.
If one but knows the Mysteries you sing.

---

[20] En Erebos Phos is a common ahistorical phrase found amongst some Hekate's devotees, witches, and practitioners. In rough Latin, it translates to, 'In Darkness, Light!'

On Gifts

Khaire Hekate Pandoteira[21]!
I lay forth my offerings, in their bounty,
And give thanks for your generosity,
That I may return this small portion to you,
Gracious Goddess,
My gratitude is poured upon the earth,
In your many names.

On the Hunt

Hekate Elaphebolos[22],
Wild Lady,
Roaming the mountains
At the side of Artemis,
That lover of deer,
Hekate Lyko[23],
At the side of the Huntress,
You dance amidst the wilderness.

---

[21] Pandoteira: All-giver/Bestower/Bounteous. An epithet given also to Demeter.

[22] Elaphebolos: Shooter of Deer.

[23] Lyko: Wolf-formed.

Aglaos[24]

Hekate Chrysosandalos,
You gentle Goddess,
Sappho places you in Love's company
For even Golden Aphrodite heeds your wisdom
Lovely Handmaid,
Blessed of all the Titans,
Radiant and True are you,
My devotions pale in comparison
To the peace you bring.
My gratitude is as bright as the stars,
Which adorns your mother's gown.

---

[24] Aglaos: Radiant/Bright/Pleasing. The term is often applied to festivity, and in the Greek Magical Papyri describes Hekate.

Springtime Blessings

Rising
Up and up and up
From darkness strange
Like warm sap
Rising along the heart
Of your baneful plants
You rise in the spring
The Kore at your side
For you heard her cries
That fateful day
It was you who spoke
Soothing the heart of Demeter
It was you who acted
When no other would
You rise
And bring forth
This salvation.

Prothyraea[25]

Hekate Trioditis, Gatekeeper,
You who stood before the Propylaia[26]
You before whom the Kharites play,
You beautiful Goddess,
Unto you I pray, I lift my voice in your honor.
You, most beloved, who shines light within my life.
Even in my darkest hour,
You have graced my path,
As a blessing, and many are your gifts.
Hekate, Blessed Goddess, for whom the Kharites spritely
dance and play.
For thousands of years, It has been your name whispered in
adoration and awe.
May it be so for a thousand more.

---

[25] Strictly speaking, the surviving use of Prothyraea is as an epithet of Diana and Eileithyia, both of whom are conflated with Hekate in Late Antiquity. It translates as 'Before the Gate' which mirrors Hekate's role as Propylaia.

[26] Propylaia: Before the Gate.

The Litany

Hekate Trimorphos[27]
Golden sandaled and saffron cloaked
Your hair woven with serpents bold.
Hekate Dadophoros[28]
In your hands
Bright torches, whips, a libation bowl.
Hekate Kleidoukhos[29]
A silver key hangs upon your girdle
Rising above us
You stride the boundaries of worlds.
Hekate Kourotrophos[30]
You reside in the hearts of midwives
Easing the labor of mothers
Soothing the cries of babes.
Hekate Brimo[31],
You are the wolf, the lion, the horses free,
With ghosts in your wake,
Howling spirits sending chills on your night.

---

[27] Trimorphos: Three-Formed. A reference to the image of Hekate as Three Maidens standing round a pillar.

[28] Dadophoros: Torchbearer. One of Hekate's primary traits in sculpture and literature has to be Her dual torches.

[29] Kleidoukhos: Keybearer. Another common trait in Hekate's cultus is Her carrying a Key. Sometimes it is the key to city gates, or the key to a temple gate, or even the key to the Underworld itself.

[30] Kourotrophos: Childnurse. A classification of Goddess who aids in pregnancy and labor, easing the process, that can also be used as an epithet.

[31] Brimo: Angry One, the Terrifying, or of Crackling Flame. This fearsome epithet can also apply to Persephone, Demeter, and Cybele.

Hekate Pyriphoites[32]
Holy fire is in your heart
Lighting the world with your torches
Horned Goddess of the Night.
Hekate Limenitikos[33]
Watching the ocean
Crash upon the shore
You overseer of the harbors.
Hekate Indalimos[34]
Tender and lovely
Erototokos and knowing you are
A blessing upon the world you are.
Hekate Charopos[35]
Brimo you are
Darkness wraps your shoulders
Fire blooms in your wake.
Hekate Bythios[36]
Eater of filth
Terrible you are
To those whom you Will.
Hekate Oistroplaneia[37]
Mistress of corpses
Queen of the dead
You who gives succor to the Restless Ones.

[32] Pyriphoites: Firewalker. Many of Hekate's appearances in The Chaldean Oracles and the Greek Magical Papyri emphasize Her connection with fire and light.

[33] Limenitikos: Of the Harbor.

[34] Indalimos: Beautiful.

[35] Charopos: Fierce/Grim/Flashing/Bright. An epithet that is closely associated with the sea, with a wide range of translations. It can also describe blue-grey eyes.

[36] Bythios: Abyssal/ Of the Deep. Another epithet that emphasizes a connection with the sea, but it also can imply an association with the Underworld.

[37] Oistroplaneia: Spreader of Madness/Causing the Wanderings of Madness. Many Gods are associated with madness, and Hekate is far from the only one.

To the Genetyllides[38]

Hail to you Kourotrophoi
Great are you
Who welcomes new life
Hekate, Artemis, Eileithyia[39]
You Genetyllides
Guarding mother and child
Easing pangs
Welcoming the first breath
Comforting the fears of fathers
Hail to you
You who live in the hearts of midwives
You Genetyllides
Hekate, Artemis, Eileithyia
Who welcomes new life
Great are you
Hail to the Kourotrophoi.

---

[38] The Genetyllides, or Kourotrophoi, are a classification of Gods who specialize in childbirth and the safety of mother and child. There are many Goddesses who fall into this category, but Hekate, Artemis, and Eileithyia are the ones I have relied on in this role.

[39] Eileithyia is a Goddess in Her own right, as well as sometimes being an epithet for Hekate in Her role as a Goddess of childbirth.

In the Beginning

Grace-filled shining night
Window into time,
Brilliant torches glance along your flesh
Red and blue and white and brown
Taking us deeper
Back
Back
Back
Where we were once
The heart of stars
Swirling in a thousand ancient galaxies
Distributed by Her wondrous Will.

Winter Promise

Rejoice and sing, for the promise is come.
Hidden in the icy wind,
In the crisp of fallen leaves.
It whispers of warmer things.
Rejoice and sing, come all together.
Stand in circle or alone,
Cherish the promise to come.
In darkness it shines as sun upon the snow.
Rejoice and sing, in the longest night.
Raise your voice, lay forth the feast,
Celebrate the candles bright.
The promise inching closer to the hearth.
Rejoice and sing, of Yule tidings,
Of ebb and flow,
Of spark and light,
Of bones and dirt,
Of breezes and the breath,
And with the dawn, a return has begun.
The promise an oath upon the very flesh of time
Though darkness wraps his cold arms around us,
And the trees and crops freeze upon the ground.
The sun will dance to strength again,
Of this promise do we sing.
Rejoice and sing, of the longest night,
When cold holds close, and darkness clings.
Rejoice and sing, of the growing light,
When the cold ground warms, and the spirit sings,
Rejoice and sing, of the promise kept.

I sing

I sing, of the far-wandering daughter,
I sing, of the torchbearing queen,
I sing, of the triple-faced maiden,
As she guides sweet Persephone.
I sing, of the restless ones 'round Her,
I sing, of the hounds who hear Her keen,
I sing, of the tree of life blooming,
As She nurses the best within me.
I sing of the gifts which She offers,
I sing of Her light I have seen,
I sing of Her splendor which awakens
As She lights my spirit with glee.

On Pergamum[40]

Holy, having slain Clytios,
Hekate, with Helios as your company,
Heavenly, you rise in the night,
Earthly, you reside in hidden places,
Enodia[41], every path is yours,
Ever watchful, you send forth virtues to us each.

Holy

Holy Goddess, shining bright,
Exalted, grace-filled,
Keys to heaven, earth, and sea
are yours to command.
A night-wandering beauty
throngs of the restless in your wake,
Eternal you are, O liminal one.

---

[40] Pergamum was an ancient city state in modern day Turkey. There stood a grand altar which depicted the war of the Gods against the Titans. Today the altar stands in the Pergamum museum in Germany. In one scene we see Hekate wielding Her torches against the Titan Clytios as She sided with the Gods against Her own kind.

[41] Enodia: Of the Road.

Present

In darkness, you are the light,
In silence, you are the song,
On ocean shore and mountainside, you are present,
Hekate with serpents in your hair,
And brazen sandals on your feet.
In heat of summer, you are restful shade,
In frozen winter, you the heat of family,
In forest depths and gardens green, you are present.
Hekate, Queen of life and death,
Of saffron robes and shining hair.
In thresholds of home, you stand as guardian.
In the doors of the city and temple, you wait with the key.
In the stars, sea, and caverns, you are present.
Hekate, most fair, leading the hounds,
Ensouling the world with your grace.

Devotional Chant

Hekate
Hekate
Hekate
Sovereign, Guardian, Guide
Be the light within my heart that inflames my Will.
Hekate
Hekate
Hekate
Guardian, Guide, Sovereign
Be the brilliance of my words that they may serve You.
Hekate
Hekate
Hekate
Guide, Sovereign, Guardian
Be the torch that leads my mind to greater Mysteries.

It is easy to customize this according to what you have going on in life by changing the epithets. I like to use it on devotional walks, or while working on devotional projects and spells.

Prayers

For Guidance

In night, twilight, dusk, and dawn.
A day that was cold turned warm,
I stand at the crossroads
Sweet offerings at my feet.
O Queen of Choices, cheer me,
Open my sight,
A torch ahead gleaming
Wolves howl within my ear
The raven comes shrieking near
The moment draws here.
O nurse and companion,
Dominion is yours
Bless me with your guidance
That the path I would walk be won.

For a Difficult Time

Torchbearing Triformis[42]
Guardian at the gate
Illuminate the path
That I might not slip
Walk before me
That I may see what might be
Walk behind me
That I may see Truth's light upon the past
Walk beside me
So that I might serve your Will
O Lady of the Threshold
Watch over me
That I may carry your light into the world.

---

[42] Triformis: Three-Formed.

For Healing

My wounds are raw, Hekate, though healing has begun.
I find my praise is cut short by the pain.
Teeth grip against each other when I summon the Will to
speak your names.
By the pain.
How can I move on?
Leaving them behind, trailing only memories, when you have
taken them away, yes, you took them away,
and so, my pain.
I shall write instead a song, of memories crafted, friendships
wrought.
Of what was lost, what was taken.
A letter perhaps, of nothing, should my words falter still.
Perhaps the wound needs time yet, before the airing can be
fulfilled.

For Blessings on the Day

Torchbearing Triformis
Guardian at the Gate.
Illumine the path.
That I might not slip.
Walk before me that I may see what might be.
Walk behind me that I might see the path with clarity.
Walk beside me that together we might work your will today.

For Protection

Hekate, smile upon my house,
Let no harm come to my family,
And ensure my ancestors
Hear my prayers for them.
Hekate, you are a light in the darkness,
A blessing for all your devotees.
As you accompany us across
The thresholds of life
Until we return to you
Beyond that final door.

For Self-Knowledge

Hekate
Most beautiful maiden
Of the ruddy feet
Goddess of the roads
I lift my gaze to you at the crossroads
at the shores
at the howling hounds' delight
Shining Queen of Beasts
Guide me
Show me the key,
The key to myself.

For Connection

Hekate, light my way,
Hekate, shine bright,
When I am in darkness, you bring peace
When I am in darkness, you bring healing,
When I am in darkness, you bring faith.
Enodia!
Hekate, light my way,
Hekate, shine bright,
When I am in darkness, you bring peace,
When I am in darkness, you bring healing,
When I am in darkness, you bring faith.
Apotropaia[43]!
Hekate, light my way,
Hekate, shine bright,
When I am in darkness, you bring peace,
When I am in darkness, you bring healing,
When I am in darkness, you bring faith.
Kleidoukhos!

*Repeat as necessary, using whatever epithets and titles come to you or you deem appropriate. This works very well while walking or as a mantra in shrine.

---

[43] Apotropaia: Averter of Evil.

For Blessings

Hekate, shine in me,
Enlighten my heart
Kalliste, you are to me,
Infinite light
Torchbearing, mother of souls,
Bless me,
Enrich the world with your bright might.

To Hear Her Again

Hekate Aglaos
Shining you are
Blinding bright
In the darkness
of my heart,
In trying times,
Your beauty graces
my simple life
A music few can hear
though I sometimes
Become deaf to it.
It enlivens my dance
through my days,
Ebbing and flowing,
Shifting my balance,
In your ever-present torchlight,
May it ever be thus.

When making a Request

Hekate Antaia[44], you of the three forms, three paths, three worlds,
In your service I have walked these years.
Offerings poured forth in libation, in voice, in flame.
I have shared your story to those who would hear.
And now, I come, hopeful...

This ends with the particulars of what I hope to be fulfilled. "Now I come hopeful that this job contract be fruitful and generous," for example.

For Seeking the Mysteries

Velvet dark sweeps above me,
Soft swirling purple and blue,
Ancestral gems sewn tight,
On the tapestry of night,
No silver moon to hide the treasures of heaven,
Nor will it ease the Earth of Her secrets.
At a path diverging, I dance,
a sounds upon my lips,
Darkness crowded thick with things unseen.
I seek Her Mysteries shining like torches,
A light no word can contain.

---

[44] Antaia: She who Meets/Besought with Prayers.

For Offerings

I pour forth my offerings
To remember the grace of you.
I whisper beauteous syllables
To trace your sacred names,
Hekate Polynomos[45].

For Blessings

I sing to the Gods of the Old Ways, in whose names I pray,
I sing to the land all around me,
To the Beloved Dead, without whom I would not be.
Thus do I dance through the seasons,
Thus the seasons dance through my life.
I sing to the Goddess around me, Enodia,
I sing to the Earth that supports me,
I sing to the Ancestors' kindness,
So do the years pass 'round me,
Though joy, and sorrow, and light.
I sing to the Gods of my household,
To the Elements which sustain me,
To those who came here before me.
Blessing my days as I go.

---

[45] Polynomos: Many Names.

For Protection

Khaire Hekate Alexeatis[46]!
You stand at the door,
Turning away all troubles,
May your guard remain,
For all my days.
In gratitude,
I lift my voice in praise!

Expressing Gratitude

Hekate Amphiprosopos[47],
Looking in all directions,
You know all that transpires.
You knew the fate of Persephone.
You stood with the Gods against the Titans.
Your brow shines with divine knowledge.
In your footsteps we aspire to walk.
Our thanks upon our lips.

---

[46] Alexeatis: Averter of Evil.

[47] Amphiprosopos: Double-Faced. This is not of the same meaning as we apply today, but refers to Hekate's ability to see in multiple directions at once.

A Daily Prayer

Hekate Kleidoukhos, Dadophoros, Kourotrophos,
Goddess of the three-ways,
Amphiphaes,
Shine bright within my heart,
within my words,
within my mind,
And deliver me from evil,
Great Goddess,
As I journey within this realm,
As above, so below,
As within, so without.
Blessed Be.
*This is my go-to daily prayer. It begins my day and ends my day,
though the first three lines change as I adjust them to my state of
mind.*

For Protection

Hekate Apotropaia, Goddess who spans all boundaries,
You who stands upon the harbor,
You who stands at the gate,
You who stands at the crossroads of our lives,
We ask that you smile upon us,
That your Will be kind to us,
That evil be turned away from us,
In your many names, we beseech you.

During Times of Despair

Hekate, Liminal Queen, Brimo,
Great Goddess unto whom I have sworn my oaths,
My offerings have been many, and I have given voice to your lore.
My heart burns with your fire, and I walk upon your paths.
Hekate Aregos[48], may your grace descend upon me, lift up my burdens.
Whisper wisdom in my ear, and let your torches diminish the darkness within me.
May your keys unchain me.
With such burdens I struggle to give you the attention you deserve.
I cannot see your light,
Nor give voice to your many names.
Hekate Aregos, Helper of Gods and mortals, be gentle,
Let your light burn away these pains.

For Wisdom

Hekate Basileia[49],
You who hold the Keys to the Whole Universe,
You most Glorious Queen, with your torches shining bright,
Upon the roads we tread.
Let our choices be true, Great Goddess.

---

[48] Aregos: Helper.

[49] Basileia: Queen.

For Help in Clearing Away a Problem

Khaire, Hekate Borborophorba[50]!
Take this detritus from my life,
Transform it to your Will,
O Goddess,
That my life be purged of its taint,
And I will bring you gifts,
Of poem and song,
Of paint and praise,
In your honor,
Full of gratitude
I will be.
If you lift this burden,
Help me cleanse this life,
Which you have given me.

---

[50] Borborophorba: Eater of Filth.

During Times of Rage

Khaire Brimo!
Queen of the Dead,
Dread Goddess,
You who pours forth your rage,
In a mighty roar of power and flame.
May I never receive that righteous anger
Which you deliver upon those who fail you.

For Insight

Khaire Hekate,
You cunning Queen of Heaven, Earth, and Sea
Let my vision be clear,
That I not fall prey to the plots of others.
Let my own plans be fruitful,
That I may turn my resources towards you.
Oh Goddess unto whom the mighty witches
Did worship and construct shrines,
In your many names,
I pray that you hear me.
I pray grant this simple prayer.
I pray.

For the Ancestors

Hekate Eidolios[51],
The Dead follow in your wake,
Restless, Untimely,
They howl our their sorrows,
And I pray to you,
Bring them to their peace.
Let my ancestors know rest,
Take them into the House of Hades,
Where their worries will fall aside,
That they might know peace,
Unto you I pray.

---

[51] Eidolios: Ghostly, Phantasmal.

For a Smooth Childbirth

Khaire Eileithyia!
May the pangs ease,
And the breath come steady,
And the birth be swift!
May the mother be blessed
With strength,
With kindness,
with health!
Eileithyia, by whatever name you prefer,
Let the child thrive strong and true,
Far beyond this passage into life,
Let the mother smile upon her oikos[52] for many years,
Let them both thrive, whole and true,
Khaire Eileithyia!
May the pangs ease,
And the breath come steady,
And the birth be swift!

---

[52] Oikos: Greek word for household.

For Justice and Wisdom

Hail unto you wise Hekate,
I pray unto you,
Stand in the Assembly,
Be a presence that brings justice and clarity,
In this time of confusion and disparity,
That those you choose might act on behalf
Of the greater good,
That the manifold injustices of the day
Be halted by your hand.
That wisdom and right actions
Be the foundation of the Assembly today.

To Honor Her

Khaire, Hekate Elateira[53]!
Beautiful Goddess of the Three Ways,
With your mighty hounds,
Of air, earth, and water.
Your powers span all realms,
Grace us with your blessings,
Great Goddess,
Daughter of Asteria and Perses,
Queen of all boundaries,
In your honor, we do pray.

---

[53] Elateira: Driver/Charioteer.

For Protection of a Loved One

Hekate Empousa[54],
who haunts day and night,
come forth from the Underworld.
You who attends the sacrifices for the Dead,
Stay your hand from those I love,
Be kind,
And many will be the offerings poured in your honor,
Oh Hekate-Empousa,
Bless us, Phantasmal Goddess.

---

[54] Empousa is usually described as a monstrous vampire like figure, and not exactly a Goddess, but the Scholiast on Apollonius Rhodius' Argonautika draws a connection between the monster and Hekate.

For Her Will to Be Favorable

Khaire Hekate!
Your light shines within,
And within all else,
Heavenly Queen,
You who brings forth virtue,
Who breathes life into the world,
Who works Her Will,
Who stands in the Heavens,
With one foot in this realm,
Mighty Hekate,
Anima Mundi[55],
Shining forth with Faith, Truth, and Love.
Unto you do I lift this praise,
You, the mighty Source,
And I, your devotee.
Hekate Megiste[56]!
In your names I pray…

---

[55] Anima Mundi: World Soul. The Chaldean Oracles in particular describes Hekate as the Source of all souls and the heart of the virtues of Faith, Truth, and Love.

[56] Megiste: The Greatest.

To Bless a Meeting

Hekate Hegemonen[57], Goddess, Queen,
Torchbearer who spans beyond all boundaries,
I ask after my good spirits,
That they who receive this offering,
Be of kindly disposition,
That Hekate Eukoline[58] bless our association,
And shine light upon me and mine.

For Mercy

Hekate Kapetoktypos[59], stay your hand, my Queen,
For deep are the wounds I bear.
More I cannot take,
Stay your hand, my Goddess,
Let my grief be lessened, the days be brighter.
Hekate Kapetoktypos,
I pray to you,
Stay your hand.

---

[57] Hegemonen: Guide.

[58] Eukoline: Good-tempered.

[59] Kapetoktypos: Tomb-disturber/Causing Lamentations.

For Blessings

Khaire Hekate Ephodia[60],
Your nature lost to the mists of time,
I seek you in all corners,
In all mysteries,
O Great Goddess Hekate,
Many are your names,
Vast your reach,
I lift up my meager light,
Hoping to join it with your brightness,
The light of thousands of your devotees,
Filling up the moonless night.
Hail unto you Hekate Ephodia!
Illuminate the truth of this mystery.

---

[60] Ephodia: unknown meaning. While the ephodia were a fund paid by a city-state for a citizen to go on a pilgrimage, and there is an inscription to Hekate Ephodia in Nemea, the precise connection with Hekate remains a mystery.

For a Peaceful Home

Hail Hekate Luko[61],
I stand in the warmth of home,
I speak your name,
Hekate Lukaina[62],
I offer you these simple prayers and gifts.
That there be peace and grace upon us.
That your ferocious guardians protect us.
That you tame the wolves who would intrude upon the peace
of home.
Hail Hekate Luko,
May you be pleased.

---

[61] Luko: Wolf-Formed.

[62] Lukaina: She-Wolf.

Poems

Untitled

Autumn settles on the land
A cloak of leaves
The last fluttering breath of Summer
Before decay sets in
Crisp air bites the skin
that yesterday was warmed by sun.

Harvest Season

At a crossroad
In the ivy, oak, and laurel
The figs and pomegranates heavy in fruit
A well devoid of relief
Steps leading into darkness
Three masks, serpent haired
Lovely visions
Observe these ghosts
Know the choice
that all who live must find
Your back upon the pillar
Keys within your hand
Lampades[63] round you dancing
to the tempo of fear
Hounds cry forth your fury
Women cry your joys
Hekate's night is nearing.

---

[63] Lampades are a classification of torchbearing Nymphs most often associated with Underworld deities like Hekate.

In the Dark

Embers red and black
Bring the darkness close
Lets the cold night whisper
Across bare skin
To become a chill weight
upon the spirit
Watching, wandering,
Too close, restless
The darkness breathes
The detritus on undisturbed earth stirs
A slip of leaves against scales unseen
The fire that once fended off
Unknown terrors
sleeps in untended coals
Letting darker spirits creep
up the spine,
A shiver.

Passing

Keys ring against the door
As I stand
threshold bound
The metal slides into darkness
Bites,
And knows freedom
The binding lock spins open
The way springs into being
I simply must choose to step.

Damnamene[64]

Delighting in shadows you walk
Abroad in the night amid tombs
Maiden, you are beautiful and fierce
Noteworthy in your reach
As you stand between all things
Might fills you as your light fills the world
Ensouler, you are also Mother,
And never shall we know your limit
Eternal, you have none.

Alpha Omega

Sprawling, slick with gore
This is the beginning,
And the end
Life is messy.

Mene[65]

Ghost light
The silver white glow of the night
Stars retreating into the darkness
Dimmed by the brilliance of you.

---

[64] Damnamene: She Who Subdues by Force.

[65] Mene: a name for the Moon.

Becoming

Soft warmth turns to passion
Burning deep inside
No flesh could soothe this fire
Nor water quench its thirst
It fills the world
Sanctifies it
With one sacred tone
It binds all things
brings all life
 up out of the first
Becoming
That most sacred Source
from which all is made
in Her shining hands
We are torches
Living the light of Her way.

Enchained

I fear what will come
The call which will shatter me
Cut me so that only strangled gasps erupt
The fear coils down
Ready with infernal glee
To bring me low
With the inevitable
Do I fear what's to come
Or is it just the waiting?

Un

Unwed,
You are the mother of million
Unbound
You are true wisdom whispered in the good king's ear
Unbent
You stood with the Gods when war came.

Untitled

Sometimes prayer is silent
Crafted from wordless pain
Bit by bloody bit
Unspoken, overwhelming.

Mystery

Graceful, well-formed Goddess
Your veil guards all mysteries
Yet lights my way.

A Thousand

A thousand lights burning
A thousand lights in the night
A thousand more by morning
A thousand voices lifting
A thousand songs rejoice
A thousand harmonies bursting.

The Work

On darkest night,
With the howl of the winds burning my lungs
Rocks strike my naked feet
Shivers hold me tight
Fading with each stride around the firelight
Sweat builds against my flesh,
Makes my gown cling in awkward drapes.
Unknowing, I am ecstasy.
Your name upon my lips,
Shouted in wintry air,
Sung into the heavens.
You fill me up,
Bursting from my heart,
Wild syllables.
A drumbeat on my soul.

On Revelation

The world opens
Revelation is a lion with a mane of umbrella seed wishes
White on the wind
No ground to seize it
Distant shores
Seeds aching for wishes granted on the wings of Zephyrs
I stand, unable to reach, to grasp, to embrace any one of them.
Afraid to see
Them falter, flicker, fade
The sun in its melody of shimmering hope and light
Never blinks,
Never fails,
Whatever the fate of lions,
The strength remains, an embrace
A kiss upon my skin following wishes I dared to dream.
Under leonine grace,
Clarity gives earthly feast
A song to dandelion dreams.

Pain

Eyes closed,
Anguished cries fill my mind.
And I see,
My body, a ball of grief,
At a crossroads,
Bleeding sorrow onto red brick.
I cling to the foot
of your icon
Blinded by loss,
Knowing your light
Unseen, yet
I feel it.
Slow, warming, burning,
Lifting my burdens,
And I mourn them.

Altar

One candle dances on the altar,
When She hears my supplications.

Sorrow

The dark moon withdraws
The ancestors grow loud
They mourn
My mother's heart is sadness
Her child withers
And I wonder if his grief at her passing
Has laid the path for him.
It breaks the heart to think.

Appendix A.

Recipes

Khernips

water   sea salt   dried bay leaf
lighter or matches

Take a deep breath, and focus your intention to create a water which is full of the powers of purification and sacred to the Gods. Take three pinches of sea salt and add them to the water:

Thus the water is purified.

Pick up the bay leaf, light it on fire. Douse it in the water:

Thus the water is blessed in the names of all the Gods.

Incense

My incense recipes are meant to be taken in pinches and burned on a charcoal disk. Those with the skills to do so could probably modify the ingredients to make cones or sticks, but these recipes are suitable for anyone with patience and a mortar and pestle. The recipes are very much my own creation, and not based on historical sources.

Recipe 1

2 parts dried bay leaf
3 pinches each of cinnamon, allspice, nutmeg and jasmine tea
1 part myrrh gum
1 part sage
3 parts dried rose petals
1 part dried white oak bark
1 tsp honey

Blend together in a mortar and pestle. Allow to dry. Store in a cool dark place.

Recipe 2

3 parts rose petals
3 dried bay leaves
1 tbsp jasmine tea
1 tsp each of cinnamon, allspice, nutmet
3 pinches of chamomile
2 tsp myrrh gum

Grind well together in a mortar and pestle. Store in a cool dark place.

Ritual Oil

1 sealable bottle
almond oil or olive oil
quartz crystal small enough to fit in the bottle

Timing: during the Perseid or Orionid meteor showers.

As Hekate is the daughter of the star Titaness, Asteria, I opt to
harness the energies in the astronomical events to create my
oil. I prefer the Perseids, for they share a name with Hekate's
Father, Perses, but other occasions can be useful too. Take
your quartz crystals outside during the meteor showers and as
you place them, ask Asteria to suffuse the stones with Her
blessings. Leave them to experience this energy overnight.
Then put them in the bottle, and pour the oil over them.
Envision the energy of the stars filling the oil and becoming
one with them.

Appendix B

Epithets

One way to get to know a deity is to learn their lore and the names that their original worshippers used to describe them. Epithets are titles that describe their traits, places of worship, or hint at the lore surrounding the God in question. My research currently covers more than 250 different names for Hekate. Here are a few of my favorites.

Alexeatis: Averter of Evil
Ameibousa: One who Transforms
Anassa Eneroi: Queen of the Dead
Antaia: She Who Meets/Is Besought with Prayers
Ariste: the Best
Brimo: Angry One/The Terrifying/Of Crackling Flames
Dadophoros: Torchbearer
Daeira: Teacher
Ekdotis: Bestower
Episkopos: Guardian/ One who Watches Over/ Overseer
Eukoline: Good-tempered
Hieros Pyr: Holy Fire
Kleidoukhos: Keeper of the Keys
Kourotrophos: Child Nurse
Kynegetis: Leader of Dogs
Lampadephoros: Lamp-bearer
Leaina: the Lioness
Megiste: the Greatest
Nykti: of the Night
Ophioplokamos: with Snaky Curls/Coiled with Snakes
Paionios: Healer
Pammetor: Mother of All
Pandoteira: All-giver/Bestower of Everything/Bounteous
Pantos Kosmou Kleidoukhos: Keeper of the Keys of the Cosmos

Pasikratea: Universal Queen
Phosphoros: Light-bearer
Physis: Nature
Propolos: She who Leads/Guide/Companion
Pyripnoa: Breathing Fire
Pyriphoitos: Firewalker
Rixipyle: She who throws down the gates
Soteira: Savior
Stratelatis: Leader of Hosts/General
Tauropos: Bull-faced
Terpsimbrotos: One who delights mortals/Gladdens mortals/Gladdens the Hearts of Men
Tetraoditis: Of the Four-Ways/Haunting Crossroads/Four-Road's Mistress
Thea Deinos: Dread Goddess
Therobromon: Roaring like a Wild Beast
Trikephalos: Three-headed
Trionymos: Triple-named
Zatheos: Divine
Zoogonos: Seed of Life
Zootrophos: Nourisher of Life

Appendix C

Hekate's devotees span the world and thousands of years. There are festivals and holy days that follow the schedule of the moon that date back to the 8th century BCE, and new ones that our modern practitioners have created. The calendar we are familiar with is very different from the lunar schedule that the Greeks followed.

Monthly Rites:

Hekate's Deipnon (Dinners):
Every Dark Moon. A time to clean house. Gather up all the dust, crud, and mess that has built up in the nooks and crannies of your home. Put together a small feast and offer it to Hekate and Her train of the Restless Dead. Traditionally, this would have been a cake, some garlic, fish, and eggs, and was not meant for human consumption. In ancient Greece, this food and detritus of the month would have been taken to a nearby three-way crossroad and left as an offering. It was considered ill luck to look back at the junction after leaving. Some noticed that the less well off, the homeless, and the outcast were often seen taking the offerings for themselves.

Today, with considerations for things like littering and the health of wildlife in your area, you'll need to decide how to celebrate this central rite according to what you and your particular situation can manage. In my case, I also take this time to tithe a small amount of money in Hekate's honor, and dedicate it to a worthy cause. This ritual was meant to purify the home and alleviate any troublesome spirits in one's life as well as honoring Hekate.

Noumenia:
When the first crescent moon appears in the sky. This is the time to honor the Gods of your household, including Hekate. Offer incense and other gifts at this time, and ask that They bless your home and family.

Festival of the Kourotrophoi:
This festival honors the Goddesses of Childbirth, including Hekate. There are three occasions when it was celebrated in the ancient world, all a few days after a particular phase of the moon. In February, that day is three days before the Deipna. In June, it is three days after the Noumenia. And lastly, in August, it is held three days after the full moon. These are good times to ask for help with fertility, with a pregnancy, for the health of your children, or to honor the milestones one's kids have attained. The ancients used this holiday to have processions of women and children carrying offerings to the sanctuaries of their local Kourotrophos.

Full Moon:
In many modern practices, Hekate is honored at the Full Moon in one way or another. It's a good time to work magic, begin devotional work. It's also a good time to double check that you're upholding any agreements you've made with Her.

Annual Festivals

The Festivals of Demeter and Kore: Because of Hekate's close
ties with Demeter and Persephone, it is likely that She had a
role in their major festivals. The Thesmophoria, celebrated in
the autumn a few days before the October full moon and
lasted three to five days. As women were the only participants
in this rite, little enough was written in the ancient world for
us to learn. We know it entailed purifications, a procession,
fasting, eating sesame cakes and honey, celebration, and a
sacrifice.

Hekate was also likely involved in the Eleusinian
Mysteries, but what we know about these rites is largely
speculative. It seems likely that Hekate was honored in these
rites as the helpful companion of Demeter and Persephone.

January 1st:
New Year's Day. Hecate and Janus, the Roman God of
transitions were closely associated in the ancient world. I
choose to honor both at the end and beginning of every year
with offerings and a request for a good year.

January 31st:
Feast Day. A modern festival to simply honor Hekate.

Her Sacred Fires: Full Moon in May. Since 2010, Sorita D'Este
has celebrated Hekate with a ritual that is celebrated the
world over. To see the ritual, go to
http://hekatecovenant.com/rite-of-her-sacred-fires/

August 13th:
This modern festival honors Hekate's more volatile aspects, and you'll read about it being associated with Her as a Storm Goddess. All of which is unrelated to the way the ancient world understood Her. Most likely, this festival sprang up because of the celebration of Diana Nemoralia at the Lake Nemi during the Ides of August. The repeated conflation of Hekate with Artemis and Diana has led many people to associate the festivals of one with the others.

October 31st:
In the contemporary Pagan world, this holiday is historically associated with the Celtic festival of Samhain, and has since been partially divorced from those roots to become a pan-Pagan celebration. Many of us take this time to honor our ancestors, and, in a Hekatean context, this is no different. Personally, I ask for Hekate's assistance in communing with my family history and the associated spirits. After all, Hekate is associated with the Dead, and has the ability to cross between all the realms.

November 16th:
Hekate's Night. These days some practitioners associate this night with Hekate as a Wild Huntress. Others simply embrace it as a good time to honor and connect with Her. I am at a loss as to this holiday's origins.

November 30th:
Crossroads Festival. Another holiday of questionable origin. Most references to it mention that it is a good night to connect with Hekate of the Crossroads. I personally find it to be a good time to re-examine goals and to contemplate my own personal crossroads and the decisions that I must make.

Life Transitions

As a Goddess of transitions and liminal spaces and times, all moments of change can be understood as being under Hekate's purview. A lot of Her devotees come into Her path during trying moments of uncertainty and change. Particularly those moments when life feels like it is too much to take, or when something new has begun, or something old has come to an end, all these are Hers. These are all good times to seek Her guidance.

Ultimately, over time you'll come up with your own approaches to creating vital fulfilling rites to honor Hekate that will be yours and a reflection of your own relationship with Her.

Appendix D

Offerings

Some of the following offerings are traditional, particularly the plants, many of which are listed in the Orphic Argonautika. Others have become common enough in some groups dedicated to Hekate in the world today. In the ancient world, most of the Gods received animal sacrifice, and Hekate is no different. The ancients offered Her black puppies, cows, goats, and I don't want to mislead you in that. However, I haven't listed it here, because many people today have no experience doing such things safely, and likely live in a place where that kind of thing is unwelcome or even illegal. Lastly, use this list as a starting point for finding your way with Her, rather than a hard list. Add to it! Experiment!

Colors
   Black
   Blue
   Dark green
   Gold
   Orange
   Red
   Violet
   White
   Yellow

Food
Absinthe
Apples
Cheesecake
Coffee
Eggs
Garlic
Herbal tea
Honey cake
Honey
Mead
Milk
Olive oil
Ouzo
Pomegranates
Red mullet fish
Retzina
Saffron
Sesame cookies
Wine

Plants

Aconite (poisonous, caution)
All-heal
Asphodel
Barley
Basil
Bay Laurel
Belladonna (poisonous)
Black Poplar
Cedar
Chamomile
Crocus
Dandelion
Fern
Fleawort
Hellebore
Henbane
Honeysuckle
Hulwort
Jasmine
Juniper
Lavender
Mandrake
Mint
Mugwort
Mushrooms
Mustard
Oak
Oak Moss
Olive
Parsley
Poppy
Red roses
Rue
Rushes
Sage

Safflower
Soapwort
Vervain
Wormwood
Yew (poisonous, caution)

Incense
Dittany of Crete
Dragon's Blood
Frankincense
Myrrh
Styrax

Stones
Amber
Amethyst
Carnelian
Jet
Lapis lazuli
Lodestone
Onyx
Meteorites/Tektite
Ruby

Symbols

      Brass
      Bronze
      Candles
      Cemetery dirt
      Copper or bronze coins
      Cow hair/hide
      Crossroads dirt
      Dog hair
      Goat hair
      Gold
      Horse hair
      Keys
      Shed snake skin
      Silver
      Torches

Bibliography:

Primary Sources:

Apollodorus. *Library*, 1.6.2.

Aristophanes. *Frogs and Other Plays (Penguin Classics)*, David Barret, trans. Penguin, 2007.

Athanassakis, Apostolos N. trans. *The Homeric Hymns: Translation, Introduction, and Notes*, Johns Hopkins, 2004.

--------. *Hesiod: Theogony, Works and Days, Shield,* Johns Hopkins, 2004.

---------. *The Orphic Hymns,* Johns Hopkins, 2013.

Euripides. *Ion,* Line 1049.

-----------. *Phoenician Women*, lines 109-110.

-----------. "Hymn to Hekate," *The Trojan Women.*

Habicht, Christian. *Pausanias' Guide to Ancient Greece (Sather Classical Lectures)*, University of California, 1999.

Hesiod. *Theogony and Works and Days*, M.L. West, trans. Oxford, 2009.

Lucian, *Pharsalia*, 4.839-40.

Ovid. *Metamorphoses (Oxford World's Classics)*, trans. A. D. Melville, Oxford, 2009.

Plato. *Six Great Dialogues (Dover Thrift Editions)*, trans. Benjamin Jowett, Dover, 2007.

Race, William R. *Apollonius Rhodius: Argonautica*, Loeb Classical Library, 2008.

Strabo, *Geography, Vol. VI, Books 13-14 (Loeb Classical Library, No. 223)*, trans. Horace Leonard Jones, Loeb, 1929.

Theocritus. *Idylls (Oxford World's Classics)*, trans. Anthony Verity, Oxford, 2008.

Virgil. *The Aeneid (Penguin Classics)*, Penguin, 2010. 4.511, 4609-610, 6.247.

West, M. L. *The Orphic Poems*, Oxford, 1983.

Academic Sources:

Alcock, S., and R. Osborne, eds. *Placing the Gods: Sanctuaries and Sacred Space in Ancient Greece*, Oxford, 1994.

Alexandrescu-Vianu, Maria. "The Treasury of Sculptures from Tomis: The Cult Inventory of a Temple," from *Dacia 53*, pp.27-46.

Alföldi, Andrew. "Diana Nemorensis," *American Journal of Archaeology,* vol. 64, no. 2, Apr. 1960, pp. 137-144.

Ankarloo, Bengt and Stuart Clark, eds. *Witchcraft and Magic in Europe, Vol. 1: Biblical and Pagan Societies*, University of Penn, 2001.

----------. *Witchcraft and Magic in Europe, Vol. 2: Ancient Greece and Rome,* University of Penn, 1999.

----------. *Witchcraft and Magic in Europe, Vol. 3: The Middle Ages,* University of Penn, 2002.

----------. *Witchcraft and Magic in Europe, Vol. 5: The Eighteenth and Nineteenth Centuries,* University of Penn, 1999.

--------------. *Witchcraft and Magic in Europe, Vol. 6: The Twentieth Century,* University of Penn, 1999.

Ateslier, Suat. "The Archaic Architectural Terracottas from Euromos and Some Cult Signs," from *Labraunda and Karia,* edited by Susanne Carlsson and Lars Karlsson (see below). pp. 279-290.

Aydaş, Murat. "New Inscriptions from Stratonikeia and its Territory," Gephyra, BAND 6, 2009, p. 113-130.

Baur, Christopher and Paul Victor. *Eileithyia*, University of Missouri, 1902.

Beard, M. and J. North, eds. *Pagan Priests*, Ithaca, 1990.

Behari, Jerusha. *Ambivalent Goddesses in Patriarchies: A comparative study of Hekate in Ancient Greek and Roman Religion and Kali in Contemporary Hinduism,* dissertation from pursuit of Ph.D. at the University of KwaZulu-Natal, 2011.

Berard, C. et al. *A City of Images: Iconography and Society in Ancient Greece*, trans. D. Lyons, Princeton, 1989.

Berg, William. "Hecate: Greek or 'Anatolian'?" from *Numen*, Vol. XXI, Fasc. 2, pp. 128-140.

Bernabe, Alberto. "The Gods in Later Orphism," in *The Gods of Ancient Greece: Identities and Transformations, Vol. 5*, edited by Jan Bremmer and Andrew Erskine, Edinburgh University, 2010, pp. 422-442.

---------. "The *Ephesia Grammata*: Genesis of a Magical Formula," in C. Faraone and D. Obbink, *The Getty Hexameters*, Oxford, 2013. pp. 71-96.

---------. *Instructions for the Netherworld: the Orphic Gold Tablets*, Brill, 2008.

Betz. Hans Dieter. *The Greek Magical Papyri in Translation, including the Demotic Spells, Vol. 1*, University of Chicago Press, 1992.

Blundell, S., and M. Williamson. *The Sacred and the Feminine in Ancient Greece*, New York, 1998.

Boardman, John and E.S. Edwards. *The Cambridge Ancient History: III part 2, The Assyrian and Babylonian Empires and Other States of the Near East, from the Eighth to the Sixth Centuries B.C.*, Cambridge, 1991.
In particular, the chapters on Anatolia pp.622 and 666 and pp 849, and Thrace on p. 591.

Boedeker, Deborah. "Hekate: A Transfunctional Goddess in the *Theogony*," *Transactions of the American Philological Association, 113*, 1983, pp. 79-93.

Boustan, Ra'anan S. and Annette Yoshiko Reed. *Heavenly Realms and Earthly Realities in Late Antique Religions*, Cambridge, 2004.

Bowden, Hugh. *Classical Athens and the Delphic Oracle: Divination and* Democracy, Cambridge, 2005.

-----------. Mystery *Cults of the Ancient World*, Princeton, 2010.

Bray, C.F.D. *Aspects of the Moon in Ancient Egypt, the Near East and Greece*, thesis in pursuit of M.A. at University of Otago, 2014.

Bremmer, Jan N. "Ancient Necromancy: Fact or Fiction?" in *Mantic Perspectives: Oracles, Prophecy and Performance* edited by Krzysztof Bielawski, Warsaw, 2015, p 119-141.

----------. "Divinities in the Orphic Gold Leaves: Eukles, Eubouleus, Brimo, Kybele, Kore and Persephone," from *Zeitschrift fur Papyrologie und Epigraphik* 187, 2013, p 35-48.

----------. *Greek Religion*, Oxford, 1994.

----------. *Interpretations of Greek Mythology*, London, 1987.

----------. "Preface: the Materiality of Magic," *The Materiality of Magic,* edited by D. Boschung and Jan Bremmer, Wilhelm Fink, 2015. p. 7-19.

British Museum Department of Coins and Medals. *A Catalogue of the Greek Coins in the British Museum,* Vol. 1-28, reprint. Nabu Press, 2011.

Brown, Christopher G. "Empousa, Dionysus and the Mysteries: Aristophanes, *Frogs* 285ff." *The Classical Quarterly (New Series),* Vol. 41, issue 01, May 1991, pp. 41-50.

Burkert, Walter. *Greek Religion,* trans. John Raffan, Wiley-Blackwell, 1991.

Burnett, Andrew et al. *Coinage and Identity in the Roman Provinces,* Oxford, 2005.

Burns, Dylan. "The Chaldean Oracles of Zoroaster, Hekate's Couch, and Platonic Orientalism in Psellos and Plethon," *Aries, vol. 6 no.2,* Leiden, 2006. p. 158-179.

Bury, J. B. *The Ancient Greek Historians*, Barnes & Noble, 2006.

Buxton, R. eds., *Oxford Readings in Greek Religion*, Oxford, 2000.

Carlsson, Susanne and Lars Karlsson. *Labraunda and Karia: Proceedings of the International Symposium Commemorating Sixty Years of Swedish Archaeological Work in Labraunda.* Uppsala Universitet, 2008.

Cartledge, Paul et al. *Religion in the Ancient Greek City,* Cambridge, 1992.

Ceccarelli, P. *Ancient Greek Letter Writing*, Oxford, 2013. p. 47-58.

Clauss, James and Sarah Iles Johnston, eds. *Medea: Essays on Medea in Myth, Literature, Philosophy and Art*, Princeton, 1997.

Clay, Jenny Strauss. "The Hecate of the *Theogony*" *GRBS* 25 (2984), pp. 27-38.

--------. *Hesiod's Cosmos*, Cambridge, 2003.

Cline, Rangar. *Ancient Angels: Conceptualizing Angeloi in the Roman Empire (Religions in the Graeco-Roman World)*, Brill, 2011.

Clinton, K. *The Sacred Officials of the Eleusinian Mysteries*, Philadelphia, 1974.

Cole, Susan Guettel. *Theoi Megaloi: the Cult of the Great Gods at Samothrace, Volumes 96-97.* Brill, 1984.

Collins, D. *Magic in the Ancient Greek World*, Malden, 2008.

Colvin, Stephen. *The Greco-Roman East: Politics, Culture, Society,* vol. 31. Cambridge, 2004.

Connelly, Joan Breton. *Portrait of a Priestess: Women and Ritual in Ancient Greece*, Princeton, 2009.

Crawford, Matthew R. "On the Diversity and Influence of the Eusebian Alliance: The Case of Theodore of Heraclea," *The Journal of Ecclesiastical History*, vol. 64, issue 2, 2013, pp. 227-257.

Damiana, K. *Sophia: Exile and Return*, UMI, 1998.

Daniel, Robert W. "Hekate's Peplos," *Zeitschrift fur Papyrologie und Epigraphik,* 72, p. 278, 1988.

Dasbacak, C. "Hekate Cult in Anatolia: Rituals and Dedications in Lagina." from *Anodos, 6/7* Trnava, 2006/2007.

Daubner, Frank. "Stratonikeia/Hadrianopolis," *The Encyclopedia of Ancient History, first edition.* Edited by Roger S. Bagnall, et al., Blackwell, 2013. p. 6425.

De Angelis, Franco. "Archaeology in Sicily 2006-2010" *Archaeological Reports 58*, Nov. 2012, pp. 123-195.

Dean-Jones, L. *Women's Bodies in Classical Greek Science,* Oxford, 1994.

Demand, N. *Birth, Death, and Motherhood in Classical Greece,* Baltimore, 1994.

Detienne, M., and J.P. Vernant. *The Cuisine of Sacrifice among the Greeks,* trans. P. Wissing, Chicago, 1989.

Dickie, M.W. *Magic and Magicians in the Greco-Roman World,* London, 2001.

Dietrich, Bernard C. "Theology and Theophany in Homer and Minoan Crete," from *Kernos* 7, 1994, p 59-74.

---------. "Oracles and Divine Inspiration," *Kernos* 3, 1990, p 157-174.

Dignas, B. *Economy of the sacred in Hellenistic and Roman Asia Minor,* Oxford, 2002.

Dillon, J.M. "Plotinus and the Chaldean Oracles," *Platonism in Late Antiquity,* S. Gersh and C. Kannengiesser, eds., 1992, pp. 131-140.

Dillon, M. *Religion in the Ancient World: New Themes and Approaches,* Amsterdam, 1996.

---------. *Pilgrims and Pilgrimage in Ancient Greece,* New York, 1997.

---------. *Girls and Women in Classical Greek Religion,* London, 2002.

Dodd, D.B., and C. Faraone, eds. *Initiation in Ancient Greek Rituals and Narratives: New Critical Perspectives,* New York, 2003.

Dodds, E.R. "Theurgy and its Relationship to Neoplatonism," *The Journal of Roman Studies, 37,* (1947), pp. 55-69.

Dominguez, Adolfo J. "Greeks in the Iberian Peninsula," in *Greek Colonisation: An Account of Greek Colonies and Other Settlements Overseas, Vol. 1,* edited by Gocha R. Tseteskhladze, Brill, 2006, p 429-505.

Dowden, K, *Death and the Maiden,* New York, 1989.

Drew-Bear, Thomas. "Local Cults in Graeco-Roman Phrygia," *Greek, Roman, and Byzantine Studies*, Vol. 17, No. 3, 1976. pp. 247-268.

Drury, Nevill. *Rosaleen Norton's Contribution to the Western Esoteric Tradition*, dissertation in pursuit of PhD at the University of Newcastle, 2008.

Easterling, P.E., and J.V. Muir, eds., *Greek Religion and Society*, Cambridge, 1985.

Edmonds, Radcliffe G. *The 'Orphic' Gold Tablets and Greek Religion: Further Along the Path*, Cambridge, 2011.

Edmunds, Lowell. *Approaches to Greek Myth*, Johns Hopkins, 1989.

Edwards, Charles M. "The Running Maiden from Eleusis and the Early Classical Image of Hekate," from *American Journal of Archaeology*, vol. 90, no. 3, (Jul., 1986), pp. 307-318.

Edwards, Mark. *Neoplatonic Saints: the Lives of Plotinus and Proclus by their Students*, Liverpool University, 2000.

Ekroth, Gunnel. "Inventing Iphigeneia? On Euripides and the Cultic Construction of Brauron," *Kernos 16*, 2003, pp. 59-118.

Errington, Robert Malcolm. *A History of Macedonia*, University of California, 1990.

Fairbanks, Arthur. "The Chthonic Gods of Greek Religion," *The American Journal of Philology*, vol. 21, no. 3, 1900, pp. 241-259.

Faraone, Christopher. *Ancient Greek Love Magic*, Cambridge, MA, 1999.

------------. *Various Acts on Ancient Greek Amulets: from Oral Performance to Visual Design*, London, 2012.

Faraone, Christopher and Dirk Obbink. *Magika Hiera: Ancient Greek Magic and Religion*, Oxford, 1997.

Faraone, C., and L. McClure, eds., *Prostitutes and Courtesans in the Ancient World*, Madison, 2006.

Farnell, Lewis Richard. *The Cults of the Greek States, Vol. II*, Clarendon Press, 1896.

Feather, Jacqueline M. *Hekate's Hordes: Memoir's Voice*, dissertation submitted in pursuit of PhD. at Pacifica Graduate Institute, 2009.

Feingold, Lawrence. "Fuseli, Another Nightmare: *The Night-Hag Visiting Lapland Witches*," *Metropolitan Museum Journal 17*, 1984, p. 49-62.

Ferguson, J. *Greek and Roman Religion: A Source Book*, Park Ridge, NJ, 1980.

----------. *Among the Gods: An Archaeological Explanation of Ancient Greek Religion*, New York, 1989.

Fischer-Hansen, Tobias and Birte Poulsen. *From Artemis to Diana: The Goddess of Man and Beast*, Museum Tusculanum Press, 2009.

Foley, H.P. *Homeric hymn to Demeter: Translation, Commentary, and Interpretive Essay*, Princeton, 1994.

Fontenrose, Joseph. *The Delphic Oracle*, Berkeley, 1978.

----------. *Didyma: Apollo's Oracle, Cult and Companions*, University of California, 1988.

---------. *Python: A Study of Delphic Myth and Its Origins*, Biblo & Tannen Publishers, 1974.

---------. *Ritual Theory of Myth*, University of California, 1971.

Fox, Robin. *Brill's Companion to Ancient Macedon: Studies in the Archaeology and History of Macedon, 650 BC - 300 AD*, Brill, 2011.

Freeman, Charles. *Egypt, Greece, and Rome: Civilizations of the Ancient Mediterranean*, Oxford, 1999.

Friedman, Leah. *Hestia, Hekate, and Hermes: An archetypal trinity of constancy, complexity, and change*, Ph.D. dissertation from Pacifica Graduate Institute, 2002.

Frothingham, A. L. "Medusa, Apollo, and the Great Mother," *American Journal of Archaeology*, Vol. 15, No. 3, Jul-Sep. 1911, pp. 349-377.

Fullerton, Mark D. *The Archaistic Style in Roman Statuary*, Bryn Mawr, 1982.

Gager, J. G. *Curse Tablets and Binding Spells from the Ancient World,* Oxford, 1992.

Gill, C., N. Postlethwaite, and R. Seaford, eds., *Reciprocity in Ancient Greece,* Oxford, 1998.

Graf, Fritz. *Magic in the Ancient World (Revealing Antiquity 10),* trans. Franklin Philip. Harvard, 1999.

Graf, Fritz and Sarah Iles Johnston. *Ritual Texts for the Afterlife: Orpheus and the Bacchic Gold Tablets,* Routledge, 2013.

Graninger, Denver. "Apollo, Ennodia, And Fourth-century Thessaly," from *Kernos* 22, 2009, p. 109-124.

Grant, F. *Hellenistic Religion,* New York, 1953.

Green, C.M.C. *Roman Religion and the Cult of Diana at Aricia,* Cambridge, 2006.

Griffiths, E. *Medea,* Routledge, 2006.

Gül, Onur. "A Group of Marble Statuettes in the Ödemiş Museum," SDU Faculty of Arts and Sciences Journal of Social Sciences, no. 32, August 2014. p. 177-196.

Hägg, R., ed., *The Iconography of Greek Cult in the Archaic and Classical Periods,* Kernos Supplement, Liege, 1992.

----------. *The Role of Religion in the Early Greek Polis,* Athens, 1996.

Harrison, Jane E. "Helios-Hades" *The Classical Review,* vol. 22, issue 1, 1908, pp. 12-16.

---------. *Themis: A Study in the Social Origins of Greek Religion,* Cambridge, 2010.

Harvey, W.J. *Reflections of the Enigmatic Goddess: The Origins of Hekate and the Development of her Character to the End of the Fifth Century B.C.,* thesis in pursuit of M.A. at University of Otago, 2014.

Heller, Katrina Marie. *Iconography of the Gorgons on Temple Decoration in Sicily and Western Greece,* dissertation in pursuit of Ph.D at University of Wisconsin-La Crosse, 210.

Hellstrom, P., and B. Alroth, eds. *Religion and Power in the Ancient Greek World,* Uppsala, 1996.

Henry, Oliver. "Karia, Karians and Labraunda," in *Mylasa/Labraunda*, 2005. p. 69-105.

Herring, Amanda Elaine, *Structure, Sculpture and Scholarship: Understanding the Sanctuary of Hekate at Lagina*, dissertation in pursuit of Ph.D at University of California, 2011.

Hinnells, John R. *A Handbook of Ancient Religions*, Cambridge, 1992.

Hogarth, D.G. *Excavations at Ephesos: The Archaic Artemisia*, London, 1908.

Holderman, E. *A Study of the Greek Priestess*, Chicago, 1913.

Holmes, William Gordon. *The Age of Justinian and Theodora*, 1912.

Humphreys, S.C. "Ancient Theologies and Modern Times," in *Kernos 25*, 2012, p 149-161.

Ireland, S. "Dramatic Structure in the *Persae* and *Prometheus* of Aeschylus," *Greece and Rome*, vol. 20, issue 2, Oct. 1973, pp. 162-168.

Jim, Theodora Suk Fong. "Naming a Gift: the Vocabulary and Purposes of Greek Religious Offerings," *Greek, Roman, and Byzantine Studies* 52, 2012, pp. 310-337.

Johnston, Sarah Iles. "Animating Statues: A Case Study in Ritual," *Arethusa* 41, 2008. pp. 445-477.

-----------. "Crossroads" *Zeitschrift fur Papyrologie und Epigraphik*, 1991, pp. 217-224.

----------. "Demeter, Myths, and the Polyvalence of Festivals," *History of Religions*, Vol. 52, No. 4, May 2013, editor Wendy Doniger, University of Chicago, 2013.

----------."The Development of Hekate's Archaic and Classical Roles in the Chaldean Oracles," dissertation in pursuit of PhD. at Cornell, 1987.

----------. "Hekate, Leto's Daughter, in OF 317," *Tracing Orpheus: Studies of Orphic Fragments*, edited by Miguel Herrero de Jauregui, et al., de Gruyter, 2011.

120

----------. *Hekate Soteira: A study of Hekate's Roles in the Chaldean Oracles and Related Literature*, American Classical Studies, 1990.
--------. *Mantike: Studies in Ancient Divination* (Religions in the Graeco-Roman World), Brill, 2005.
--------. *Religions of the Ancient World*, Harvard, 2004.
--------. *Restless Dead: Encounters between the Living and the Dead in Ancient Greece*. Univ. of California, 2013.
----------. "Whose Gods are These? A Classicist Looks at Neopaganism," *Dans le laboratoire de historien des religions*, edited by Francesca Prescendi, et al, Labor et Fides, 2011. p. 123-133.
Johnston, Sarah Iles and Timothy J. McNiven. "Dionysos and the Underworld in Toledo," *Museum Helveticum 53*, 1996. pp. 25-36.
Jordan, D.R. "P.Duk.inv. 230, an Erotic Spell," in *Greek, Roman, and Byzantine Studies 40*, 1999, p 159-170.
Just, R. *Women in Athenian Law and Life*, New York, 1989.
Kerenyi, Karl. *Dionysos: Archetypal Image of Indestructible Life*, trans. Ralph Manheim, Princeton, 1996.
----------. *Eleusis: Archetypal Image of Mother and Daughter*, trans. Ralph Manheim, Princeton, 1991.
--------. *Gods of the Greeks*, Thames & Hudson, 1980.
--------. *The Religion of the Greeks and Romans*, Thames and Hudson, 1962.
Kitchell, Jr., Kenneth F. "Man's best friend? The changing role of the dog in Greek society," in *PECUS. Man and Animal in Antiquity*, Sept. 2002, pp. 177-182.
Kotansky, Roy and Jeffrey Spier. "The 'Horned Hunter' on a Lost Gnostic Gem," HTR 88, 3, 1995. pp. 315-37.
Kraemer, Ross Shepard. *Women's Religions in the Greco-Roman World: A Sourcebook*, Oxford, 2004.
Laale, Hans Willer. *Ephesus (Ephesos): An Abbreviated History from Androclus to Constantine XI*, West Bow Press, 2011.
Larson, Jennifer. *Ancient Greek Cults: A Guide*, Routledge, 2007.

Latura, George. "The Cross Torch of Eleusis: Symbol of Salvation in the Ancient World," from a proposal to *Coin News*, 2014.

----------. "Plato's X & Hekate's Crossroads: Astronomical Links to the Mysteries of Eleusis," from *Mediterranean Archaeology and Archaeometry, Vol. 14, No.3*, 2014, pp. 37-44.

Lefkowitz, M.R. *Heroines and Hysterics*, London, 1981.

----------. *Women in Greek Myth*, Baltimore, 1986.

----------. *Greek Gods, Human Lives*, New Haven, 2003.

Lefkowitz, M.R. and M.B. Fant, *Women's Life in Greece and Rome: A Source Book in Translation*, Baltimore, 1982.

Leonard, Miriam. "Tragedy and the Seductions of Philosophy," *The Cambridge Classical Journal*, vol. 58, Dec. 2012, pp. 145-164.

Lesser, Rachel. "The Nature of Artemis Ephesia," *Hirundo: The McGill Journal of Classical Studies, Vol. IV*, 2005/2006, pp. 43-54.

Liapis, Vayos J. "Zeus, Rhesus, and the Mysteries," *The Classical Quarterly*, vol. 57.02, Dec. 2007, pp. 381-411.

Lima, R. *Stages of Evil: Occultism in Western Theater and Drama*, University of Kentucky, 2005. (particularly pp. 225 chapter titled The Cave and the Magician.)

Limberis, Vasiliki. *Divine Heiress: The Virgin Mary and the Creation of Christian Constantinople*, Routledge, 1994.

Locke, Liz, "Orpheus and Orphism: Cosmology and Sacrifice at the Boundary," in *Folklore Forum* 28:2, 1997, p 3-23.

Lo Monaco, Annalisa. "Feast and Games of the Paides in the Peloponnese of the Imperial Period," *Roman Peloponnese III: Society, Economy and Culture under the Roman Empire: Continuity and Innovation*, edited by C.E. Lepenioti and A.D. Rizakis, ΜΕΛΕΤΗΜΑΤΑ 63 for the Research Institute for Greek and Roman Antiquity of the National Hellenic Research Foundation, Athens, 2010. pp. 309- 327.

Luck, Georg. *Arcana Mundi: Magic and the Occult in the Greek and Roman Worlds: A Collection of Ancient Texts,* Johns Hopkins, 2006.

Magliocco, Sabina. "Aradia in Sardinia: The Archaeology of a Folk Character," *Ten Years of Triumph of the Moon,* Hidden Pub, 2009. pp. 40-61.

-----------. *Witching Culture: Folklore and Neopaganism in America,* University of Penn, 2004.

Majercik, Ruth. *The Chaldean Oracles: Text, Translation and Commentary,* Prometheus Trust, 2013.

----------. "Chaldean Triads in Neoplatonic Exegesis: Some Reconsiderations," from *The Classical Quarterly, New Series,* vol. 51, No. 1 (2001), pp. 265-296.

Malkin, I. *Religion and Colonization in Ancient Greece,* New York, 1987.

Mander, Pietro. "Hekate's Roots in the Sumerian-Babylonian Pantheon according to the Chaldean Oracles," *Religion in the History of European Culture: Proceedings of the 9th EASR Annual Conference and IAHR Special Conference 14-17 September 2009, Messina,* edited by Giulia Sfameni Gasparro, Augusto Cosentino and Mariangela Monaca. Officina di studi Medievali, 2013, pp. 115-132.

Marquardt, Patricia A. "A Portrait of Hecate," *The American Journal of Philology,* vol. 102, no. 3 (Autumn, 1981), pp. 243-260.

Mayor, Adrienne. "Grecian Weasels" *The Athenian,* Feb. 1989. pp. 22-24.

McClure, Laura K. (ed.), *Sexuality and Gender in the Classical World: Readings and Sources,* Blackwell Pub, 2002.

Meadows, A. R. "Stratonikeia in Caria: the Hellenistic City and its Coinage," *The Numismatic Chronicle,* Vol. 162, 2002, pp. 79-134.

Meister, Michael W. "Multiplicity on the Frontier: Imagining the Warrior Goddess." *Pakistan Heritage* 2, 2010, pp. 87-98.

Meyer, Marvin W. *The Ancient Mysteries: A sourcebook*, University Penn, 1999.

Mikalson, Jon. D. *Ancient Greek Religion*, Wiley-Blackwell, 2009.

---------. *Athenian Popular Religion*, UNC, 1987.

--------. *Religion in Hellenistic Athens*, Berkeley, 1998.

Miles, M.M. *The City Eleusinion, Agora*, vol. 31, Princeton, 1998.

Mitchell, Stephen and Peter Van Nuffelen. *One God: Pagan Monotheism in the Roman Empire*, Cambridge, 2010.

Mitropoluos, Elpis. *Triple Hekate mainly on votive reliefs, coins, gems, and amulets*. Atenas, 1978.

Momigliano, A. ed. *The Conflict between Paganism and Christianity in the Fourth Century*, Oxford, 1963.

Mooney, Carol M. *Hekate: Her Role and Character in Greek Literature from before the Fifth Century B.C.*, dissertation in pursuit of a Ph.D. at McMaster University, 1971.

Murray, Alexander Stuart. *A History of Greek Sculpture down to the age of Pheidias (and his successors)*, vol. 2, Oxford, 1883.

Mylonopoulos, Joannis. "Hellenistic Divine Images and the Power of Tradition," from *Hellenistic Sanctuaries Between Greece and Rome*, edited by Milena Melfi and Olympia Bobou, Oxford, 2016, p 106-127.

Mylonos, G. E. "Eleusis and the Eleusinian Mysteries," from *The Classical Journal* 43(3), 1947. p. 130-146.

Newton, Charles Thomas and R. Popplewell Pullan. *A History of discoveries at Halicarnassus, Cnidus and Branchidae, Vol. II*, Austrian National Library, 1862.

Nevett, L.C. *House and Society in the Ancient Greek World*, Cambridge, 1999.

Nilsson, M.P. *A History of Greek Religion*, Oxford, 1925.

---------. *Greek Popular Religion*, New York, 1940.

---------. *The Dionysiac Mysteries of the Hellenistic and Roman Age*, Lund, 1957.

Nixon, Shelly M. *Hekate: Bringer of Light*, California Institute of Integral Studies, 2013.

Noegel, Scott and Joel Walker, eds. *Prayer, Magic, and the Stars in the Ancient and Late Antique World*, Penn State, 2010.

Oakley, J., and R. Sinos, *The Wedding in Ancient Athens*, Madison, 1993.

Ogden, Daniel. *Magic, Witchcraft and Ghosts in the Greek and Roman Worlds: A Sourcebook*, Oxford, 2009.

Ogle, M. B. "The House-Door in Greek and Roman Religion and Folklore," *The American Journal of Philology*, vol. 32, no. 3, (1911), pp. 251-271.

Oikonomides, Al. N. "Records of 'The Commandments of the Seven Wise Men,' in the 3rd c. B.C.: the Revered 'Greek Reading-book,' of the Hellenistic World." *Classical Bulletin*, 63, 1987, pp. 67-76.

Otto, Walter F. *Dionysus: Myth and Cult*, trans. Robert Palmer, Indiana University, 1995.

Pachoumi, Eleni. "The Erotic and Separation Spells of the Magical Papyri and *Defixiones*," in *Greek, Roman, and Byzantine Studies 53*, 2013, p 294-325.

Palinkas, Jennifer Lynne. *Eleusinian Gateways: Entrances to the Sanctuary of Demeter and Kore at Eleusis and the City Eleusinion in Athens*, dissertation in pursuit of PhD at Emory, 2008.

Panaite, Adriana. "Protective Deities of Roman Roads," in *Jupiter on Your Side: Gods and Humans in Antiquity in the Lower Danube* edited by Christina-Georgeta Alexandrescu, Institutul de arheologie 'Vasile Pârvan' Bucharest, 2013, p 133-142.

Parke, H.W. *Festivals of the Athenians*, London, 1977.

-------. *The Oracles of Apollo in Asia Minor*, London, 1985.

Parke, H.W., and D.E.W. Wormell, *The Delphic Oracle*, 2 vols. Oxford, 1956.

Parker, Robert. "Greek Religion," *The Oxfrod History of Greece and the Hellenistic World*, edited J. Boardman et al., Oxford, 1991. pp. 306-329.

---------. *Athenian Religion: A History*, Oxford, 1996.

----------. *Miasma: Pollution and Purification in Early Greek Religion,* Oxford, 1990.

----------. *Polytheism and Society in Ancient Athens,* Oxford, 2005.

Patton, K. *Religion of the Gods: Ritual, Reflexivity, and Paradox,* Oxford, 2007.

Platt, Verity. *Facing the Gods: Epiphany and Representation in Graeco-Roman Art, Literature and Religion,* Cambridge, 2011.

Pomeroy, S.B. *Goddesses, Whores, Wives, and Slaves: Women in Classical Antiquity,* New York, 1975.

Price, S.R.F. *Rituals and Power: The Roman Imperial Cult in Asia Minor,* Cambridge, 1984.

------------. *Religions of the Ancient Greeks,* Cambridge, 1999.

Pulleyn, S. *Prayer in Greek Religion,* Oxford, 1993.

Rabinowitz, Jacob. *Rotting Goddess: The Origins of the Witch in Classical Antiquity.* Autonomedia, 1998.

Reeder, E.D., ed. *Pandora: Women in Classical Greece,* Princeton, 1995.

Richter, Gisela M. A. "A Bronze Relief of Medusa," from *The Metropolitan Museum of Art Bulletin,* Vol. 14, No. 3, (Mar., 1919), pp. 59-60.

Ricl, Marijana. "Phrygian Votive Steles," *Epigraphica Anatolica,* HEFT 33, 2001, pp. 195-198.

Rigsby, Kent J. "Chrysogone's Mother," *Museum Helveticum 60,* 2003, pp. 60-64.

Ronan, Stephen. *The Goddess Hekate,* Chthonios, 1992.

Rüpke , Jörg. *The Individual in Religions of the Ancient Mediterranean,* Oxford, 2013.

Rose, H. J. "Orientation of the Dead in Greece and Italy," *The Classical Review,* vol. 34.7, Nov. 1920, pp. 141-146.

Rosivach, V. *The System of Public Sacrifice in Fourth-Century Arhens,* Atlanta, 1994.

Rouse, W.H.D. *Greek Votive Offerings,* Oxford, 1902.

Rousel, P. *Delos,* Paris, 1925.

Sanchez Natalias, C. "The Bologna Defixio(nes) Revisited," *Zeitschrift fur Papyrologie und Epigraphik* 179, 2011. pp. 201-217.

Scott, Michael. *Space and Society in the Greek and Roman Worlds,* Cambridge, 2012.

Scullion, Scott. "Euripides and Macedon, or the Silence of the *Frogs*," *The Classical Quarterly,* vol. 53, issue 2, Dec. 2003, pp. 389-400.

Seaford, R. *Reciprocity and Ritual*, Oxford 1994.

----------. *The Bacchae*, Oxford, 1996.

Serfontein, Susun M. *Medusa: From Beast to Beauty in Archaic and Classical Illustrations from Greece and South Italy,* thesis presented in pursuit of a Masters at Hunter College of the City University of New York, 1991.

Sergis, Manolis G. "Dog Sacrifice in Ancient and Modern Greece: From the Sacrifice Ritual to Dog Torture (kynomartyrion)," *Folklore,* 2010, pp. 61-88.

Seznec, J. *The Survival of the Pagan Gods*, trans. Barbara Sessions, Princeton 1953.

Sgambati, Lynne. *Hekate: Faces and Phases of the Transformation Goddess,* dissertation in pursuit of a PhD. at Pacifica Graduate Institute, 1995.

Siapkas, Johannes. "Karian Theories," *LABRYS*, Uppsala, 2013.

Simms, Robert. "Agra and Agrai," *Greek, Roman, and Byzantine Studies 43*, 2002/3, pp. 219-229.

Skinner-La Porte, Melissa. "Snakes on a Mane: Medusa, the Body and Serpentine Monstrosity," paper presented at the Monsters and the Monstrous Conference at Oxford, 2010 on behalf of the University of Guelph.

Söğüt, B. "Naiskoi from the Sacred Precinct of Lagina Hekate Augustus and Sarapis," from *Anados* 6/7, 2006/2007, p. 421-431.

--------. "Stratonikeia," *Turkey through the Eyes of Classical Archaeologists: 10th Anniversary of Cooperation between Trnava University and Turkish Universities,* Trnava, 2014. pp. 27-37.

Sourvinou-Inwood, C. *"Reading" Greek Culture: Texts and Images, Rituals and Myths,* Oxford, 1991.

--------. *"Reading" Greek Death. To the End of the Classical Period,* Oxford, 1995b.

Stallsmith, Allaire B. "The Name of Demeter Thesmophoros," *Greek, Roman, and Byzantine Studies 48,* 2008, pp. 115-131.

Suarez, Rasiel. *ERIC: The Encyclopedia of Roman Imperial Coins,* Dirty Old Coins, 2005.

--------. *ERIC II: The Encyclopedia of Roman Imperial Coins,* Dirty Old Coins, 2010.

Tarn, W.W. *The Greeks in Bactria and India,* Cambridge, 1938.

Taylor, Thomas. *The Eleusinian and Bacchic Mysteries,* Amazon reprint, 1891.

Thaniel, George. *Themes of Death in Roman Religion and Poetry,* thesis in pursuit of M.A. at McMaster University, 1971.

Themelis, P.G., *Brauron: Guide to the Site and to the Museum,* Athens, 1971.

Tirpan, Ahmet A. "The Temple of Hekate at Lagina," from *Dipteros und Pseudodipteros. Bauhistorische und archaologische Forschungen.* (BYZAS, Vol. 12), Phoibos Verlag, 2012.

Trombley, Frank R. *Hellenic Religion and Christianization, C. 370-529,* Brill, 1993.

Turkilsen, Debbie and Joost Blasweiler, "Medea, Cytissorus, Hekate, They all Came from Aea," Arnhem, 2014.

Turner, John D. "The Figure of Hecate and Dynamic Emanationism in the Chaldean Oracles, Sethian Gnosticism and Neoplatonism," *The Second Century Journal 7;4* . 1991. pp. 221-232.

Van Bremen, Riet. "The Demes and Phylai of Stratonikeia in Karia," *Chiron Bd. 30,* C.H. Beck, 2000. pp. 389-401.

Van Straten, F. *Heira Kala: Images of Animal Sacrifice*, Leiden, 1995.

Vermaseren, M.J. *Cybele and Attis: The Myth and the Cult*, trans. A.M.H. Lemmers, London, 1977.

Vernant, J.-P. *Myth and Society in Ancient Greece*, Paris, 1980.

Versnel, H.S. *Inconsistencies in Greek and Roman Religion II: Transition and Reversal in Myth and Ritual*, Studies in Greek and Roman Religion 6.2, 1993.

Vidal-Naquet, P. *The Black Hunter: Forms of Thought and Forms of Society in the Greek World*, Baltimore, 1986.

Von Dongen, Erik. "The Extent and Interactions of the Phrygian Kingdom," *From Source to History: Studies on Ancient Near Eastern Worlds and Beyond*, edited by Daniele Morandi Bonacossi, et al. Ugarit-Verlag, 2014. pp. 697-711.

Von Rudloff, Ilmo Robert. *Hekate in Ancient Greek Religion*, Horned Owl Pub, 1999.

Warr, George C. W. "The Hesiodic Hekate," *The Classical Review*, vol. 9.08, Nov. 1895, pp. 390-393.

West, David Reid. *Some Cults of Greek Goddesses and Female Daemons of Oriental Origin: especially in relation to the mythology of goddesses and daemons in the Semitic world*, dissertation in pursuit of a Ph.D. at University of Glasgow, 1990.

West, M.L. *Hesiodic Catalogue of Women*, Oxford, 1985.

Wilkinson, T. *Persephone Returns: Victims, Heroes and the Journey from the Underworld*, Pagemill Press, 1996.

Williamson, Christina. "City and Sanctuary in Hellenistic Asia Minor: Sacred and Ideological Landscapes," from Bolletino di Archeologia On Line, volume speciale for the Roma 2008 - International Congress of Classical Archaeology, in Callaborazione con AIAC (Associazione Internazionale di Archeologia Classica, Rome, 2010.

----------. "Civic Producers at Stratonikeia: the Priesthoods of Hekate at Lagina and Zeus at Panamara," *Cities and Priests: Cult personnel in Asia Minor and the Aegean islands from the Hellenistic to the Imperial Period,* edited by Marietta Horster and Anja Klockner, De Gruyter, 2013. pp. 209-246.

----------. "Karian, Greek or Roman? The layered identities of Stratonikeia at the sanctuary of Hekate at Lagina," from *TMA* 50, 2013. p. 1-6.

----------. "Light in Dark Places: changes in the application of natural light in sacred Greek architecture," from *Pharos,* vol. 1, 1993.

----------. "The Miracle of Zeus at Panamara: myth, mimesis and memory in the civic ideology of Stratonikeia," KNIR, 2011, University of Groningen, powerpoint.

----------. "Panamara: The (mis)fortunes of a Karian Sanctuary," from *Historische Erfgoed,* Groniek, 2009. pp. 211-218.

----------. "Putting women in their place in Pergamon," *TMA* 16, 1996, pp. 4-14.

----------. "Sanctuaries as turning points in territorial formation: Lagina, Panamara and the development of Stratonikeia," *Manifestationene von macht und hierchien in stadtraum und landschaft,* edited by Felix Pirson, *BYZAS* 13, 2012. pp. 113-150.

----------. "Shining Saviors: The role of the cults of Hekate at Lagina and Zeus at Panamara in building the regional identity of Stratonikeia," *Oud Historici Dag,* Amsterdam, 2012.

Wilson, Lillian M. "Contributions of Greek Art to the Medusa Myth," from *American Journal of Archaeology,* Vol. 24, No. 3 (Jul-Sep, 1920), pp. 232-240.

Winkle, J. *Daemons, Demiurges, and Dualism: Apuleius' 'Metamorphoses' and the Mysticism of Late Antiquity,* UMI, 2002.

Practitioner's Sources:

Bebout, Tinnekke. *Dance of the Mystai,* Pagan Writer's Press, 2013.
Bebout, Tinnekke and Hope Ezerins. *The Hekate Tarot,* self-published, 2015.
Brannen, Cyndi. *Keeping Her Keys,* Moon Books, 2019.
Carlson, K. *Life's Daughter/Death's Bride: Inner Transformations through the Goddess Demeter/Persephone,* Shambhala, 1997.
Conner, Randy P. "Come, Hekate, I Call You to My Sacred Chants," published only on Academia.edu.
Crowfoot, Greg. *Crossroads,* Aventine Press, 2005.
Crowley, Aleister. *Moonchild,* Weiser, 1970.
D'Este, Sorita. *Artemis: Virgin Goddess of the Sun & Moon: a Comprehensive Guide to the Greek goddess of the Hunt, Her Myths, Powers and Mysteries,* Avalonia, 2005.
-------. *Circle for Hekate, Vol. 1: History & Mythology,* Avalonia, 2017.
-------. *Hekate Liminal Rites: A study of the rituals, magic and symbols of the torch-bearing Triple Goddess of the Crossroads,* Avalonia, 2009.
-------. *Hekate: Her Sacred Fires,* Avalonia, 2010.
-------. *Hekate: Keys to the Crossroads: A collection of personal essays, invocations, rituals, recipes and artworks,* Avalonia, 2006.
-------. *Horns of Power: Manifestations of the Horned God: An Anthology of Essays exploring the Horned Gods of Myth and Folklore, Ancient History through to ModernTimes,* Avalonia, 2011.
Domenic, H. "Who is Hecate?" *The Beltane Papers* 47, Winter 2009/2010. pp. 9-12, 17-18.
Ford, Michael. *Book of the Witch Moon: Chaos, Vampiric & Luciferan Sorcery,* Succubus, 2006.
------. *Magick of the Ancient Gods: Chthonic Paganism and the Left Hand Path,* Succubus, 2009.

George, Demetra. *Mysteries of the Dark Moon: The Healing Power of the Dark Goddess*, Harper Collins, 1992.

Georgitsis, Tina. "Hekate's Khernips" in *Askei Kataskei 7*, 2004.

----------. "Hekate" in *The Australian Pagan Magazine 1*, 2013.

----------. "Hekate's Deipnon" in *The Alternative Spirit Magazine 1*, 2014.

----------. "Hekate and the Blessed Dead" in *The Alternative Spirit Magazine 4*, 2014.

----------. "Hekate and the Sea" in *The Alternative Spirit Magazine 6*, 2015.

----------. "Hekate's Fire" in *The Alternative Spirit Magazine 8*, 2015.

----------. "Hekate: Goddess and Mistress of Witchcraft (Classical)" in *The Alternative Spirit Magazine 5*, 2015.

---------. "Hekate in the Home" in *The Alternative Spirit Magazine 10*, 2016.

--------. "Hekate on the Shore" in *The Alternative Spirit Magazine 12*, 2016.

----------. "Hymns for Hekate" in *The Australian Pagan Magazine 2*, 2013.

--------. "Noumenia with Hekate" in *The Alternative Spirit Magazine 2*, 2014.

Grimassi, Raven. *The Witches' Craft: The Roots of Witchcraft*, Llewellyn, 2002.

Jade Sol Luna. *Hecate I: Death, Transition and Spiritual Mastery*, 2008.

-------. *Hecate II: The Awakening of Hydra*, 2009.

Keller, M.L. *Greek Goddess Traditions and the Eleusinian Mysteries: Spiritual Resources for Today*, 2012, In Press.

Marx, E. *Junkyard of the Classics*, Invisible Books, 2006. (Ellipsis Marx is an alias for Rabinowitz.)

Miller, Jason. *Protection and Reversal Magick*, Weiser, 2006.

Mishev, Georgi. *Thracian Magic: Past and Present*, Avalonia, 2012.

Oates, Shani. *A Paean for Hekate*, Lulu, 2012.

Panopoulos, Christos Pandion, et al. *Hellenic Polytheism: Household Worship, Vol. 1*, Labrys, 2014.

Payne, Kenn. *Askei Kataskei: the Official Covenant of Hekate ezine*, vols. 1-6, Covenant of Hekate, Lulu, 2013-2014.

Perdue, Jason. *Hecate's Womb (and other Essays)*, Lulu, 2011.

Rabinowitz, J. *The Rotting Goddess: The Origin of the Witch in Classical Antiquity*, Autonomedia, 1998.

Reynolds, Tara. *Hekate: Goddess Connections Workbook*, Kindle, 2013. (17 pages).

Ruickbie, Leo. *Witchcraft Out of the Shadows: A Complete History*, Hale, 2004.

Sanchez, Tara. *The Temple of Hekate: Exploring the Goddess Hekate through Ritual, Meditation and Divination*, Avalonia, 2011.

Sannion. *Bearing Torches: a Devotional Anthology for Hekate*, Bibliotheca Alexandrina, 2009.

Smith, Mark Alan. *Queen of Hell*, Ixaxaar, 2010.

-------. *The Red King*, Ixaxaar, 2011.

Spretnak, Charlene. *Lost Goddesses of Early Greece: A Collection of Pre-Hellenic Myths*, Beacon, 1992.

Tate, Karen. *Sacred Places of Goddess: 108 Destinations*. CCC Pub, 2006.

Taylor-Perry, Rosemarie. *The God who Comes: Dionysian Mysteries Revisited*, Algora, 2003.

Varner, Gary R. *Hekate: The Witches' Goddess*, Lulu, 2011.

Vermeule, Emily. *Aspects of Death in Early Greek Art and Poetry*, University of California, 1979.

Winter, Sarah Kate Istra. *Kharis: Hellenic Polytheism Explored*, 2008.

For Public Consumption:

Evslin, Bernard. *Hecate (Monsters of Mythology)*, Chelsea House Pub, 1988.

Jonson, Ben. *Sad Shepherd*, Forgotten, 2012.

Keats, John. "On the Sea," published online at:
    http://www.bartleby.com/333/509.html
Marlowe, Christopher. *Doctor Faustus*, Dover, 1994. Act III,
    Scene 2.
Shakespeare, William. *A Midsummer Night's Dream (Folger
    Shakespeare Library)*, Simon & Schuster, 2004. Act V,
    Scene 1.
----------. *Hamlet*, Simon & Schuster, 2003. Act III, Scene 2.
----------. *Henry IV, Part 1*, Simon & Schuster, 2005. Act III, Scene
    2.
----------. *King Lear*, Simon & Schuster, 2005. Act I, Scene 1.
----------. *Macbeth*, Simon & Schuster, 2003. Act III, Scene 5 and
    Act IV, Scene 1.

Index

Printed in Great Britain
by Amazon

76894579R00095